Contents

2 The Creative Spirit

Teen Novels and Short Stories, Fantasy, Humor, Mystery and Suspense, Poetry, the Arts...

14 Science

Animals, Mind and Body, Brain Food, Ancient Stones and Bones, Planet Earth...

18 Here and Now

Love and Sex, Getting it Together, Overcoming Odds, LGBTQ: Being Gay, War and Peace, Remarkable People....

27 One World

Native Americans, Latinos, Black America, Other Countries...

36 Action and Adventure

Do-It-Yourself, Sports, True Adventure...

Action-Packed Stories **38**
Africa **27**
AIDS **18**
The Americas **30**
Ancient Stones and Bones **17**
Art: Vision Becomes Image **4**
Asia **28**
Athletes **37**
Brain Food **14**
The Changing Scene **22**
Crime and Justice **20**
Do-It-Yourself **36**
Do You Believe? **18**
Drugs **19**
Europe **29**
Fantasy **3**
Fur, Feathers and Scales **15**
Getting It Together **20**
Graphic Novels **5**
Historical Fiction **13**
Horror **7**
Humor **2**
Latinos **31**
LGBTQ: Being Gay **21**
Looking Good **21**
Love and Sex **21**
Make Up Your Mind **22**
The Middle East **27**
Mind and Body **16**
The Movies and TV **8**
Mystery and Suspense **6**
Native Americans **29**
Never Again: The Holocaust **25**
New York, NY **35**
Novels and Short Stories **11**
On Stage **4**
Overcoming Odds **23**
Planet Earth **16**
Poetry **7**
The Power of Words **18**
Rap, Rock and Bach **12**
Remarkable People **23**
Science Fiction **2**
Sports **37**
Teen Novels and Short Stories **8**
True Adventure **39**
U.S.A.: Black America **32**
U.S.A.: The Civil War and After **34**
U.S.A.: Coming to America **31**
U.S.A.: The New Nation **34**
U.S.A.: Past, Present and Future **33**
The Universe and Beyond **14**
War and Peace **24**
The Way Things Work **17**
Wheels and Wings **36**
Women **26**
Working **25**
Young Love **5**

W9-CSN-015

The Creative Spirit

Humor

ANONYMOUS AS TOLD TO TUCKER SHAW
*Confessions of a Backup Dancer
Simon Pulse
A crazy summer around a pop diva

EHRENHAFT, DANIEL
*10 Things to Do Before I Die
Delacorte
Ted, making the most of his last 24 hours

FRIEDMAN, PETER
*Ideal Marriage
Permanent
Teen in the 50s with sex on the brain

HIAASEN, CARL
Hoot
Knopf
Life in Florida enlivened by baby owls

KEMP, KRISTEN
*The Dating Diaries
Push
Making up for lost time after a break-up

KORMAN, GORDON
*Son of the Mob: Hollywood Hustle
Hyperion
The family's influence on Vince's LA life

LIMB, SUE
*Girl, 15, Charming but Insane
Delacorte
Pursuing love despite lack of confidence

LUBAR, DAVID
Dunk
Clarion
The twisted world of a wisecracking clown

MASH, ROBERT
How to Keep Dinosaurs
Weidenfeld & Nicolson
For pets, crowd control or dinoburgers

MCGRUDER, AARON
A Right to be Hostile
Three Rivers
Boondocks comics, poking fun at everyone

O'KEEFE, SUSAN HEYBOER
*Death by Eggplant
Roaring Brook
Dreams of cooking and a flour baby

RALLISON, JANETTE
*Life, Love, and the Pursuit of Free Throws
Walker
Going head-to-head with your best friend

RENNISON, LOUISE
*Away Laughing on a Fast Camel
HarperTempest
Life after the Sex God leaves

SEELY, HART, COMPILER AND EDITOR
Pieces of Intelligence
Free Press
Secretary Rumsfeld's words of wisdom

STUDIO KAIJU
*Kaiju Big Battel
Hyperion
Guide to giant city-crushing monsters

THOMPSON, JULIAN F.
Hard Time
Atheneum
In reform school with a magical doll

Science Fiction

COLFER, EOIN
*The Supernaturalist
Hyperion
Fighting parasites on future Earth

DUPRAU, JEANNE
*The People of Sparks
Random House
Making a new life on Earth's surface

FOON, DENNIS
*Freewalker
Annick
Roan and Stowe learning to use power

FOSTER, ALAN DEAN
*Lost and Found
Ballantine
Camping out leads to kidnapping by aliens

GOOBIE, BETH
*Flux
Orca
Chased by a gang into another dimension

LAWRENCE, MICHAEL
*A Crack in the Line
Greenwillow
His mother is alive in an alternate world

LOWRY, LOIS
*Messenger
Houghton Mifflin
Matty, risking all to find his true name

OPPEL, KENNETH
*Airborn
EOS
Life on an airship leads to adventure

REED, KIT
*Thinner Than Thou
TOR
Thin and fit becomes a dangerous religion

REEVE, PHILIP
*Predator's Gold
EOS
Hester, selling out a city for revenge

RUCKER, RUDY
*Frek and the Elixir
TOR
Quest to restore Earth's lost species

SCHMITZ, JAMES H.
*The Witches of Karres
Baen
Whose power can stop an alien invasion

STAHLER, DAVID, JR.
*Truesight
EOS
Cursed with sight in
a blind world

VALENTINE, JAMES
*Jump-Man
Simon & Schuster
Time-traveling Theo wrecks
Jules' romance

WERLIN, NANCY
*Double Helix
Dial
Eli uncovering his own
genetic secrets

ZAHN, TIMOTHY
***The Green and
the Gray**
TOR
Aliens at war on New York
City streets

Fantasy

BARRY, DAVE AND
RIDLEY PEARSON
***Peter and the
Starcatchers**
Disney Editions
Fearless Peter before Neverland

BATH, K. P.
***The Secret of Castle
Cant**
Little, Brown
Powerful, dangerous knowledge

BOYLE, FIONNA
***A Muggle's Guide to
the Wizarding World**
ECW Press
Exploring the Harry Potter
Universe

CADNUM, MICHAEL
*Starfall
Scholastic
When the gods ruled

CONSTABLE, KATE
*The Singer of All Songs
Arthur A. Levine
Calwyn, using ice magic
chantments

DALE, ANNA
*Whispering to Witches
Bloomsbury
A missing page from a book
of magic

DE LINT, CHARLES
*Blue Girl
Viking
17 and trying to avoid trouble

DICKINSON, JOHN
*Cup of the World
David Fickling
Loving a man met in her dreams

DUNKLE, CLARE B.
*Close Kin
Henry Holt
Seeking love on a quest

FARMER, NANCY
*The Sea of Trolls
Atheneum
Lucky Jack kidnapped by Vikings

FARREN, MICK
*Kindling
TOR
The Four, challenging the
Dark Things

FINDLAY, JAMIESON
*The Blue Roan Child
Scholastic
Searching for stolen colts

FISHER, CATHERINE
*The Oracle Betrayed
Greenwillow
Seeking the religious leader's heir
*Snow-walker
Greenwillow
Fighting an evil foreign tyrant

HALE, SHANNON
*Enna Burning
Bloomsbury
Fires to warm and to destroy

LACKEY, MERCEDES
*The Fairy Godmother
Luna
Fixing magical messes

LE GUIN, URSULA K.
*Gifts
Harcourt
Wonderful, useful and
deadly talents

MAHY, MARGARET
*Alchemy
Margaret K McElderry
Magic versus free will

MCKILLIP, PATRICIA A.
*Alphabet of Thorn
Ace
An orphan girl haunted by
an ancient tale

MCNAUGHTON, JANET
*An Earthly Knight
HarperCollins
A suitable suitor for Jenny

NIFFENEGGER, AUDREY
**The Time
Traveler's Wife**
MacAdam/Cage
Lovers misplaced in time

PRATCHETT, TERRY
*A Hat Full of Sky
HarperCollins
Tiffany, aided by the Wee
Free Men

PRICE, SUSAN
*A Sterkarm Kiss
EOS
Finding romance back in
the 16th c.

PRUE, SALLY
*The Devil's Toenail
Scholastic
Starting a fire to join
a gang

PULLMAN, PHILIP
**The Amber
Spyglass**
Knopf
Will Lyra save her world
or destroy it?

RABE, JEAN
***The Finest
Creation**
TOR
Perfect beings aiding
mankind

RANDALL, DAVID
*Clovermead
Margaret K. McElderry
Lies about the past

The Secret Hour

BY SCOTT WESTERFELD
EOS, 2004

The air outside sparkled, shimmering like a snow globe full of glitter.

Jessica blinked and rubbed her eyes, but the galaxy of hovering diamonds didn't go away.

There were thousands of them, each suspended in the air as if by its own little invisible string. They seemed to glow, filling the street and her room with the blue light. Some were just inches from the window, perfect spheres no bigger than the smallest pearl, translucent as beads of glass.

Jessica took a few steps backward and sat down on her bed.

"Weird dream," she said aloud, and then wished she hadn't. It didn't seem right saying that. Wondering if she were dreaming made her feel more… awake somehow. And this was already too real: no unexplained panic, no watching herself from above, no feeling as if she were in a play and didn't know her lines—just Jessica Day sitting on her bed and being confused.

And the air outside full of diamonds.

Attitude!

BY KATHARINE DAVIS FISHMAN

Jeremy P. Tarcher/ Penguin, 2004

At ten minutes of ten on this first Saturday in August 2001, the front hall at The Ailey School is totally quiet, though not uninhabited. A few teenage girls wearing large numbers on their leotards walk silently in and out of the studios that abut the hall, talking to parents who wait outside. Inside Studio 3, some fifty more numbered teenage girls are stretching on the floor and at the barre, whispering to one another, sipping from water bottles, or sitting cross-legged beside their backpacks, meditating. Aside from their undisputable trimness, they vary in size and shape; their hair is short or pinned up in some sort of bun and occasionally corn-rowed. About two-thirds appear African-American the rest are everything else.

No one smiles. Though the heat hasn't quite kicked in yet, it is going to be a scorcher—one of those heavy, humid dog days that mark late summer in New York—and none of these studios is air-conditioned.

After twenty minutes, four godlike individuals glide in and the dancers come to attention.

eight young dancers
come of age at the ailey school

attitude!

katharine davis fishman

SEDGWICK, MARCUS
*The Book of Dead Days
Wendy Lamb
Searching graveyards to save his life

STEWART, PAUL AND CHRIS RIDDELL
*Beyond the Deepwoods
David Fickling
When Twig left the Deepwoods path

STROUD, JONATHAN
The Amulet of Samarkand
Miramax
When magicians ruled Great Britain

THOMSON, CELIA
*The Fallen
Simon Pulse
Surviving a 200 foot drop

WESTERFELD, SCOTT
*The Secret Hour
EOS
In danger when time freezes

WILLIAMS, MAIYA
*The Golden Hour
Amulet
A portal to revolutionary France

On Stage

BALANCHINE, GEORGE AND FRANCIS
101 Stories of the Great Ballets
Anchor
From Giselle to Duo Concertant

BLACKWOOD, GARY
Shakespeare's Scribe
Dutton
Surviving the Black Plague

CHEANEY, J. B.
The Playmaker
Knopf
16th C. theater apprentice facing danger
The True Prince
Knopf
Crime in Shakespeare's theater

COOPER, SUSAN
King of Shadows
Margaret K. McElderry
Nat, transported to the 16th century

DOWD, OLYMPIA
A Young Dancer's Apprenticeship
Twenty-First Century
On tour at 14 with the Moscow City Ballet

FISHMAN, KATHARINE DAVIS
*Attitude!
Jeremy P. Tarcher/Penguin
Eight teen dancers from The Ailey School

FREEDMAN, RUSSELL
Martha Graham
Clarion
She created a new kind of dance

GLOVER, SAVION
Savion
Morrow
My life in tap

JAY, ANNIE
Stars in Your Eyes... Feet on the Ground
Theatre Directories
A practical guide for teen actors

JONES, BILL T. AND SUSAN KUKLIN
Dance
Hyperion
A choreographer moves through space

KATZ, WELWYN WILTON
Come Like Shadows
Coteau
Summer stock dream job or nightmare?

LANE, ERIC AND NINA SHENGOLD, EDITORS
*Under Thirty
Vintage
Plays for a new generation

MAYBARDUK, LINDA
The Dancer Who Flew
Tundra
Rudolf Nureyev, remembered by a friend

O'CONNOR, ROSALIE
*Getting Closer
Univ. Press of Florida
Behind the scenes at the ballet

PACKER, TINA
*Tales From Shakespeare
Scholastic
Ten of the Bard's best

PORTER, TRACEY
A Dance of Sisters
Joanna Cotler
The beauty, pain and danger of ballet

ROSE, PHILIP
You Can't Do That on Broadway!
Limelight Editions
Producing A Raisin in the Sun

ROSEN, MICHAEL AND JANE RAY
*Shakespeare's Romeo and Juliet
Candlewick
A beautiful retelling

SIMMONS, DANNY, EDITOR
Russell Simmons Def Poetry Jam on Broadway & More
Atria
The energy and impact of the spoken word

TEACHOUT, TERRY
*All in the Dances
Harcourt
Balanchine, a brief life

Art: Vision Becomes Image

ARONSON, MARC
Art Attack
Clarion
Avant garde artists on the cutting edge

CHALMERS, CATHERINE
FoodChain
Aperture
Eat or be eaten

**COCKCROFT, JAMES
D., ASSISTED BY JANE
CANNING**
Latino Visions
Watts
Contemporary artists of
the Americas

FLY
Peops
Soft Skull
Stories and drawings of
real people

GHERMAN, BEVERLY
Ansel Adams
Little Brown
America's legendary photographer

GOULART, RON
Comic Book Culture
Collectors
Everyone's old favorites

GREENBERG, JAN
Vincent van Gogh
Delacorte
The mad Dutch genius

**GREENBERG, JAN
AND SANDRA JORDAN**
Action Jackson
Roaring Brook
The creative Mr. Pollack
***Andy Warhol**
Delacorte
Fabulous Prince of Pop
Runaway Girl
Abrams
The artist Louise Bourgeois

HARING, KEITH
Dogs
Bulfinch
Words and drawings of the
bold artist

**HIGHSMITH, CAROL M.
AND TED LANDPHAIR**
**America's Engineering
Marvels**
Gramercy
Masterworks to inspire

HOYE, JACOB
Boards
Universe
The art and design of
the skateboard

KASSINGER, RUTH G.
Ceramics
Twenty-First Century
From magic pots to
man-made bones

ROBBINS, TRINA
From Girls to Grrrlz
Chronicle
Nearly 60 years of women
in comics

RUBIN, SUSAN GOLDMAN
Margaret Bourke-White
Abrams
Pictures were her life

SCHIAFFINO, MARIAROSA
Goya
Peter Bedrick
Painting royal portraits and
the political scene

SCHULKE, FLIP
Witness to Our Times
Cricket
Life as a photojournalist

SPATE, VIRGINIA
Degas
SourceBooks
Acute observer of beauty

SUTHERLAND, PETER
***Autograf**
powerHouse
Photos of NYC graffiti writers

**TATHAM, CAROLINE
AND JULIAN SEAMAN**
Fashion
Barron's
A guide for the aspiring artist

Graphic Novels

**BILAL, PIERRE AND
ENKI BILAL**
***Townscapes**
Humanoids/DC Comics
Stories of small towns
fighting back

DROOKER, ERIC
Blood Song
Harvest Books
Fleeing horror, finding love

**JEMAS, BILL AND BRIAN
MICHAEL BENDIS**
***Ultimate Spider-Man
Collection**
Marvel
The tales retold for a
new generation

**GAIMAN, NEIL, ANDY
KUBERT AND RICHARD
ISANOVE**
***Marvel 1602**
Marvel
X-Men in the 17th Century

HYUN, YOU
***Faeries' Landing, Vol. 1**
Tokyopop
Ryang, 16, guardian to
a grounded fairy

JOHNS, GEOFF
***Teen Titans:
A Kid's Game**
DC Comics
Proving their worth to the
Justice League

KINDT, MATT
***2 Sisters**
Top Shelf
Danger and tragedy for Elle,
a WWII spy

**RUCKA, GREG, ED
BRUBAKER AND MICHAEL
LARK**
***Gotham Central:
In the Line of Duty**
DC Comics
To be a cop in Batman's town

**RUCKA, GREG, DREW
JOHNSON AND RAY SNYDER**
***Wonder Woman:
Down to Earth**
DC Comics
Diana's beliefs leave her open
to attack

SHANOWER, ERIC
***Age of Bronze
Sacrifice, Vol. 2**
Image
What the Greeks must do to
defeat Troy

SPIEGELMAN, ART
***In the Shadow of
No Towers**
Pantheon
An artist scarred by
September 11

**WILLINGHAM, BILL,
MARK BUCKINGHAM AND
STEVE LEIALOHA**
***Fables: Animal Farm**
Vertigo
Death stalks fairy tale refugees

Young Love

BURNHAM, NIKI
***Royally Jacked**
Simon Pulse
Problems with loving a prince

CHESHIRE, SIMON
***Kissing Vanessa**
Delacorte
Shy-guy-likes-gorgeous-girl story

FLAKE, SHARON G.
***Who Am I Without Him?**
Jump at the Sun/Hyperion
Girls and the boys in their lives

FRANK, HILLARY
***I Can't Tell You**
Graphia
When "just friends" isn't enough

JOHNSON, ANGELA
The First Part Last
Simon & Schuster
Turning 16, becoming a father

LEVITHAN, DAVID
***The Realm of
Possibility**
Knopf
The endless ways kids connect

SANDOVAL, LYNDA
***Who's Your Daddy?**
Simon Pulse
Guy-repellent parents
challenging romance

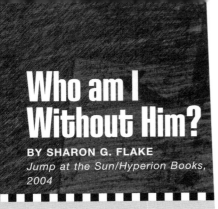

Who am I Without Him?

BY SHARON G. FLAKE

Jump at the Sun/Hyperion Books, 2004

PEOPLE SAY THINGS about me. Bad things. Momma says I give 'em reason to. That if I would just be a good girl — like the girls who wait for the bus with me in the mornings — then things wouldn't go so hard for me. But I don't wanna be like them girls: so plain and pitiful, boys don't even look their way or ask their names. I wanna be me. Ain't nothing wrong with that. Is it?

Me and them girls been standing on the same corner waiting for the same bus for a year now, and I don't even know their names. But I hate 'em just the same, mostly 'cause that girl with the red hair and gray eyes looks like the girl Raheem once left me for. She was a good girl too, so they say. She got straight A's worked in the principal's office, headed up the cheerleading team, and played flute for the marching band. You'd figure a girl like that wouldn't be no thief. But she was. She stole my man right from under me — for a little while, anyhow.

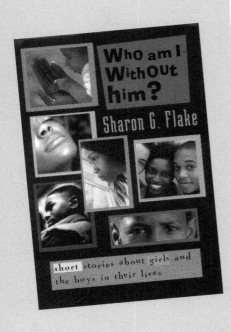

SCHREIBER, ELLEN
Vampire Kisses
HarperCollins
Outcast goth-girl seeks love with bite

SHAW, TUCKER
Flavor of the Week
Hyperion
Cooking up romance with the wrong guy

SUTHERLAND, TUI T.
***This Must be Love**
HarperCollins
Sorting out confusing relationship

WILLIAMS-GARCIA, RITA
Every Time a Rainbow Dies
HarperCollins
A victim of rape changes Thulani's life

WOODSON, JACQUELINE
***Behind You**
Putnam's
Moving on after losing a loved one

ZUSAK, MARKUS
Getting the Girl
Arthur A. Levine
Wanting the one his brother used to have

Mystery and Suspense

ADAMSON, ISAAC
Dreaming Pachinko
Perennial
Has-been rock stars, blackmail and ghosts

ALPHIN, ELAINE MARIE
Picture Perfect
Carolrhoda
Ian, unable to remember what happened

BARRETT, TRACY
Cold in Summer
Henry Holt
New town, new friends, old ghosts

BOWLER, TIM
Storm Catchers
Margaret K. McElderry
Ella, kidnapped by a vengeful ghost

CABOT, MEG
Haunted
HarperCollins
A live guy giving Suze nightmares

COLLIER, JAMES LINCOLN
***The Empty Mirror**
Bloomsbury
When two souls claim one body

CORMIER, ROBERT
The Rag and Bone Shop
Delacorte
Murder — true or false confession?

GILES, GAIL
***Playing in Traffic**
Roaring Brook
Shy Matt and the wild goth-girl

HADDIX, MARGARET PETERSON
Escape From Memory
Simon & Schuster
Family secrets hidden in Kira's brain

HARWOOD, JOHN
***The Ghost Writer**
Harcourt
Family secrets or creative writing?

KARR, KATHLEEN
The 7th Knot
Marshall Cavendish
Miles and Wick rescuing art and the valet

LANSDALE, JOE R.
A Fine Dark Line
Warner
Stanley, losing innocence, not his life

LIPPMAN, LAURA
Every Secret Thing
Morrow
Babies disappearing in Baltimore

MCALPINE, GORDON
Mystery Box
Cricket
Falling in love and solving crimes

MCNAMEE, GRAHAM
Acceleration
Wendy Lamb
Duncan stalking a serial killer

MORGENROTH, KATE
***Jude**
Simon & Schuster
Surviving an unfair, stiff sentence

OATES, JOYCE CAROL
Freaky Green Eyes
HarperTempest
Watching her parents head toward tragedy

PETERS, ELIZABETH
***Guardian of the Horizon**
William Morrow
A dangerous return to Egypt

PLUM-UCCI, CAROL
The She
Harcourt
Disappearing parents swallowed by the sea

PRIESTLEY, CHRIS
Death and the Arrow
Knopf
Gruesome serial killings in 1715

WATSON, JUDE
***Premonitions**
Scholastic
Gracie, using ESP to save her friend

WEATHERLY, LEE
***Missing Abby**
David Fickling
When a 13-year old girl vanished

WINSPEAR, JACQUELINE
***Birds of a Feather**
Soho
A runaway heiress or a murderer?
Maisie Dobbs
Soho
A private investigator's lost love

Horror

ALLIE, SCOTT, EDITOR
*The Dark Horse Book of Witchcraft
Dark Horse
Powerful women, supernatural skill

BLOOR, EDWARD
*Story Time
Harcourt
Where testing is the work of the devil

CREEDON, CATHERINE
Blue Wolf
HarperCollins
Trapped in an animal's body

HINTON, S. E.
*Hawkes Harbor
TOR
Jamie, tough enough to reform a vampire

HOFFMAN, NINA KIRIKI
A Stir of Bones
Viking
Breaking free of abuse with ghostly help

HURSTON, ZORA NEALE, COLLECTOR; ADAPTED BY JOYCE CAROL THOMAS
*The Skull Talks Back and Other Haunting Tales
HarperCollins
Spooky tales from folklore

JOHNSON, KATHLEEN JEFFRIE
*A Fast and Brutal Wing
Roaring Brook
Mentally ill or shape shifters?

KLAUSE, ANNETTE CURTIS
Blood and Chocolate
Laurel Leaf
Runs with werewolves, howls for meat boy

MCKINLEY, ROBIN
Sunshine
Berkley
Saving herself from being a vampire meal

METZ, MELINDA
*Raven's Point
HarperCollins
Ancient evil on a small island

NOYES, DEBORAH, EDITOR
*Gothic!
Candlewick
Ten original dark tales

RICE, ANNE
Interview with the Vampire
Ballantine
Vampire tells all to reporter

SAUL, JOHN
*Black Creek Crossing
Ballantine
Life in a charming, haunted house

SLEATOR, WILLIAM
*The Boy Who Couldn't Die
Amulet
The boy who could kill

SOSNOWSKI, DAVID
*Vamped
Free Press
When there are more vampires than humans

STRAUB, PETER
lost boy lost girl
Random House
A serial killer or a ghost?

VANDE VELDE, VIVIAN
Companions of the Night
Harcourt Brace/Jane Yolen
Ethan drinks the blood of humans

WALLACE, RICH
Restless
Viking
Running track with a ghost

WOODING, CHRIS
*The Haunting of Alaizabel Cray
Orchard
Terror in the London streets

Poetry

ACHEBE, CHINUA
*Collected Poems
Anchor
Nigeria's powerful writer

ALVAREZ, JULIA
*The Woman I Kept to Myself
Algonquin
Wise and personal words

COLLINS, BILLY, EDITOR
Poetry 180
Random House
An anthology of contemporary work

ESPADA, MARTÍN
Alabanza
Norton
A Latino lyric voice

GREENBERG, JAN, EDITOR
Heart to Heart
Abrams
The beauty of art and language

JANECZKO, PAUL B., EDITOR
*Blushing
Orchard
Expressions of love

JORDAN, A. VAN
*M-A-C-N-O-L-I-A
Norton
Story of a spelling whiz

JUSTICE, DONALD
*Collected Poems
Knopf
The master of simple, classical form

LANSANA, QURAYSH ALI
*They Shall Run
Third World
Harriet Tubman, woman and warrior

MOSS, THYLIAS
*Slave Moth
Persea
An enslaved girl imagining freedom

MYERS, WALTER DEAN
*Here in Harlem
Holiday House
Honoring his hometown

NYE, NAOMI SHIHAB
*Is This Forever, Or What?
Greenwillow
Texas inspiring artists and writers

PAWLAK, MARK AND DICK LOURIE, EDITORS WITH RON SCHREIBER AND ROBERT HERSHON
*Shooting the Rat
Hanging Loose
Stories and poems by high school writers

PEACOCK, MOLLY, ELISE PASCHEN AND NEIL NECHES, EDITORS
Poetry in Motion
Norton
100 poems from NYC subways and buses

PERDOMO, WILLIE
Smoking Lovely
Rattapallax
Our Nuyorican laureate

PINSKY, ROBERT AND MAGGIE DIETZ, EDITORS
*An Invitation to Poetry
Norton
From the Favorite Poem Project

REDDY, SRIKANTH
*Facts for Visitors
Univ. of California Pr.
Traditional and experimental work

SCHMIDT, ELIZABETH AND KEVIN YOUNG
Poems of New York
Random House
The icons of our city

SCHULTZ, PHILIP
*Living in the Past
Harcourt
Rochester, New York, in the fifties

SESHADRI, VIJAY
*The Long Meadow
Graywolf
From India to Brooklyn

SHANGE, NTOZAKE,
FRANK STEWART,
AND KAMOINGE INC.
***The Sweet Breath
of Life**
Atria
Words, images:
the African-American family

VECCHIONE, PATRICE,
EDITOR
***Revenge and
Forgiveness**
Henry Holt
Timeless human desires

WILLARD, NANCY
*In the Salt Marsh
Knopf
Mysteries of the natural world

WRITERSCORPS
*Paint Me Like I Am
HarperTempest
Lively teen voices

YOUNG, KEVIN
Jelly Roll
Knopf
Jazzy blues poems

The Movies and TV

ALEXANDER, GEORGE
**Why We
Make Movies**
Broadway
Black filmmakers talking

BIZONY, PIERS
Digital Domain
Billboard
Creating special effects

BOGLE, DONALD
Primetime Blues
Farrar, Straus and Giroux
The changing roles of blacks
on TV

CARTWRIGHT, NANCY
**My Life as a
10-Year-Old Boy**
Hyperion
Behind the scenes at
"The Simpsons"

DUNCAN, JODY
Star Wars: Mythmaking
Del Rey
Behind the scenes with
color photos

LUMME, HELENA
Great Women of Film
Billboard
Actresses, producers, directors,
and more

RICHMOND, RAY
*This is Jeopardy!
Barnes & Noble
Celebrating America's favorite
quiz show

ROEPER, RICHARD
**10 Sure Signs a Movie
Character is Doomed,
and Other Surprising
Movie Lists**
Hyperion
The best, the worst and more

RUBIN, SUSAN GOLDMAN
Steven Spielberg
Abrams
Crazy for movies since he was
a child

TAYLOR, HACKFORD,
JAMES L. WHITE AND
LINDA SUNSHINE
*Ray
Newmarket
A tribute to Ray Charles

VAZ, MARK COTTA
The Art of Star Wars
Del Rey
Episode II: Attack of the clones.

WORMSER, RICHARD
**To the Young
Filmmaker**
Watts
Conversations with working
filmmakers

Teen Novels and Short Stories

ADOFF, JAIME
***Names Will Never
Hurt Me**
Dutton
High school hell, a year after
a killing

AIDINOFF, ELSIE V.
*The Garden
HarperTempest
Adam and Eve and the
Serpent makes three

ALMOND, DAVID
*The Fire-Eaters
Delacorte
Bobby's world on the brink
of destruction

BATHURST, BELLA
*Special
Mariner
The chilling meanness of girls
in a group

BENNETT, CHERIE AND
JEFF GOTTESFELD
*A Heart Divided
Delacorte
Culture shock when Kate
moves South

BROOKS, KEVIN
*Kissing the Rain
The Chicken House
A witness to murder

BRUGMAN, ALYSSA
*Walking Naked
Delacorte
The power of the clique

CABOT, MEG
*Teen Idol
HarperCollins
When a film star challenges
Jim's talents

CALETTI, DEB
***Honey, Baby,
Sweetheart**
Simon & Schuster
Bad boy + quiet girl = trouble

CART, MICHAEL, EDITOR
***Rush Hour: Volume 1,
Sin**
Delacorte
Stories, essays, poetry on
one theme
***Rush Hour: Volume 2,
Bad Boys**
Delacorte
Stories, essays, poetry on
one theme

CASSIDY, CATHY
*Dizzy
Viking
Reuniting with her hippy mom

CHOLDENKO, GENNIFER
***Al Capone Does
My Shirts**
Putnam's
Growing up on Alcatraz Island

CLARK, CATHERINE
*The Alison Rules
HarperTempest
Trying to handle life's surprises

COHN, RACHEL
*Pop Princess
Simon & Schuster
Sudden stardom at 16

CORRIGAN, EIREANN
*Splintering
Scholastic
A shattered family after an attack

CREECH, SHARON
*Heartbeat
Joanna Cotler
How Annie fits into the rhythm
of life

CUMMINGS, PRISCILLA
*Red Kayak
Dutton
A tragedy that Brady may
have caused

CURTIS, CHRISTOPHER
PAUL
*Bucking the Sarge
Wendy Lamb
When your mother is a slum lord

DESSEN, SARAH
The Truth About Forever
Viking
Facing the future after a father's death

DHAMI, NARINDER
Bindi Babes
Delacorte
3 cool sisters and their interfering aunt

FLINN, ALEX
Nothing to Lose
HarperTempest
Hiding the truth about his father's death

FORDE, CATHERINE
Fat Boy Swim
Delacorte
Famous for his size, with a hidden talent

FRAUSTINO, LISA ROWE, EDITOR
Don't Cramp My Style
Simon & Schuster
Stories about that time of the month

FREDERICKS, MARIAH
Head Games
Richard Jackson
Friendship following online role playing

FRIEND, NATASHA
Perfect
Milkweed
Coping with an eating disorder

FUSCO, KIMBERLY NEWTON
Tending to Grace
Knopf
Cornelia's hidden strengths

GARDNER, GRAHAM
Inventing Elliot
Dial
Chosen for a secret society of bullies

HAUTMAN, PETE
Godless
Simon & Schuster
The power of belief in a water tower

HEMPHILL, STEPHANIE
Things Left Unsaid
Hyperion
When a good girl is led astray

HERMES, PATRICIA
Summer Secrets
Marshall Cavendish
Mama's madness and other challenges

HITE, SID
The King of Slippery Falls
Scholastic
Searching for fish, finding his identity

HOBBS, VALERIE
Letting Go of Bobby James, or How I Found My Self of Steam
Frances Foster
Life after an abusive marriage

HRDLITSCHKA, SHELLEY
Kat's Fall
Orca
Uncovering truth and learning about love

JOHNSON, ANGELA
Bird
Dial
Runaway girl searching for her stepfather

JOHNSON, MAUREEN
The Key to the Golden Firebird
HarperCollins
Sisters coping with their father's death

KADOHATA, CYNTHIA
Kira-Kira
Atheneum
Sisters' friendship, love and loss

KANTOR, MELISSA
Confessions of a Not It Girl
Hyperion
Senior year blues in Brooklyn

KOERTGE, RON
Margaux with an X
Candlewick
Gorgeous tough chick and oddball geek

KOJA, KATHE
The Blue Mirror
Farrar, Straus and Giroux
A destructive relationship with a runaway

KONIGSBURG, E. L.
The Outcasts of 19 Schuyler Place
Atheneum
Finding beauty in what is unique

KWASNEY, MICHELLE D.
Baby Blue
Henry Holt
Struggling to protect her family

LION, MELISSA
Swollen
Wendy Lamb
Samantha's race toward happiness

LYNCH, CHRIS
The Gravedigger's Cottage
HarperCollins
Where death haunts a family by the sea

MACKLER, CAROLYN
Vegan Virgin Valentine
Candlewick
Control freak ready to break out

MCCAFFERTY, MEGAN, EDITOR
Sixteen
Three Rivers
Stories about that sweet/bitter birthday

MCCORD, PATRICIA
Pictures in the Dark
Bloomsbury
An unbearable life with insane rules

Godless

BY PETE HAUTMAN
Simon & Schuster, 2004

YOU DON'T BELIEVE ANY OF THIS, DO YOU? Do you really think that I think the St. Andrew Valley water tower is the all-powerful, all-seeing ruler of all-that-is? Let me ask you something. Do you think every single person sitting in, say, your local church (or temple or mosque or coven or whatever the hell it is your parents drag you to) believes everything they hear? What about the guy who goes to church on Sunday but cheats on his taxes. That's a sin, right? If he truly believed in God, would he sin?

But that doesn't mean the tax cheat isn't religious. Religious is a whole different kettle of fish, as my grandmother would say. *I'm* religious. And I'm *serious*. Serious as a heart attack (Grandma again). Chutengodianism is important to me. But that doesn't mean I think that a big steel tank propped up on a few I-beams is omnipotent. I might be a religious zealot, but I'm not crazy.

How I Live Now

BY MEG ROSOFF
Wendy Lamb Books, 2004

We were completely clueless about how safe we'd be walking around out here. One of the soldiers I'd talked to said there were hundreds of people heading into the countryside away from the action in order to try to disappear and wait out the trouble which suggested it would be like walking around in a shopping mall. On the other hand I got the feeling that there were more than enough footpaths in England and the average refugee wouldn't be interested in socializing. The soldier's theory was that most of the people we were likely to meet would be English people but he also said that doesn't mean that they won't shoot you on sight.

I couldn't really believe that a whole bunch of enemy soldiers were going to spend their spare time crashing around in the undergrowth looking for stray people to shoot but it still seemed like a good idea to keep a low profile for as long as possible or at least while you were pretty sure the world had lost its mind.

MCDONALD, JANET
*Brother Hood
Frances Foster
From Harlem to prep school

MANNING, SARRA
*Guitar Girl
Dutton
Unexpected pop stardom

MARCHETTA, MELINA
*Saving Francesca
Knopf
Her complex relationship with her mother

MORIARTY, JACLYN
*The Year of Secret Assignments
Arthur A. Levine
Diaries, letters, notes between friends

MYERS, WALTER DEAN
*Shooter
Amistad/HarperTempest
Tragic tale of troubled teens

NELSON, BLAKE
*Rock Star Superstar
Viking
From jazz geek to rock god

PASCAL, FRANCINE
*The Ruling Class
Simon & Schuster
Upsetting the balance of power

PECK, RICHARD
*Past Perfect, Present Tense
Dial
Stories and tips on how to write them

PECK, ROBERT NEWTON
*Bro
HarperCollins
A family pulled apart and drawn together

PETERSEN, P. J. AND IVY RUCKMAN
*rob&sara.com
Delacorte
A close relationship via email

QUALEY, MARSHA
*Too Big a Storm
Dial
Brady, finding her way in the 60s

RAPP, ADAM
*Under the Wolf, Under the Dog
Candlewick
Struggling to cope with a violent past

ROBERTS, WILLO DAVIS
*Blood on His Hands
Atheneum
On the run, seeking his father's help

ROSOFF, MEG
*How I Live Now
Wendy Lamb
The bonds that form in a time of war

SHAW, SUSAN
*The Boy from the Basement
Dutton
Enduring the horrors of abuse

SHUSTERMAN, NEAL
*The Schwa Was Here
Dutton
Being friends with an unnoticeable boy

SONES, SONYA
*One of Those Hideous Books Where the Mother Dies
Simon & Schuster
Starting over in LA with a movie-star dad

STRASSER, TODD
*Can't Get There from Here
Simon & Schuster
A tribe of homeless teens on NYC streets

STRAUSS, LINDA LEOPOLD
*Really, Truly, Everything's Fine
Marshall Cavendish
Learning the truth about a family crisis

TASHJIAN, JANET
*Vote for Larry
Henry Holt
Josh's recipe for getting elected

TOWNLEY, RODERICK
*Sky
Richard Jackson
Cool jazz for a young NYC pianist in 1959

TRUEMAN, TERRY
*Cruise Control
HarperTempest
The "normal" kid with a disabled brother

VIZZINI, NED
*Be More Chill
Hyperion
Transformed by a pill from dork to hottie

WILLIAMS, JULIE
*Escaping Tornado Season
HarperTempest
Piecing together a new life after loss

WINSTON, SHERRI
*Acting
Marshall Cavendish
A twin sister claiming her own identity

WITTLINGER, ELLEN
*Heart on My Sleeve
Simon & Schuster
Challenge of a long-distance relationship

WOODS, BRENDA
*Emako Blue
Putnam's
Remembering a bright star of South Central LA

WYATT, MELISSA
*Raising the Griffin
Wendy Lamb
Thrust into the role of Rovenia's prince

ZEISES, LARA M.
*Contents Under Pressure
Delacorte
The happiness and confusion of being 14

Novels and Short Stories

AMIDON, STEPHEN
Human Capital
Farrar, Straus and Giroux
Teens and their families
facing tragedy

BERLIN, ADAM
Belmondo Style
St. Martin's
On the run from the NYC police

BEZMOZGIS, DAVID
Natasha and Other Stories
Farrar, Straus and Giroux
Immigrant lives in Toronto

BLOCK, BRETT ELLEN
The Grave of God's Daughter
William Morrow
A shameful secret hidden at
great cost

BOHJALIAN, CHRISTOPHER A.
Before You Know Kindness
Shaye Areheart
When Charlotte shot her father

BRAFF, JOSHUA
The Unthinkable Thoughts of Jacob Green
Algonquin
Learning to rebel from
his brother

CALDWELL, IAN AND DUSTIN THOMASON
The Rule of Four
Dial
Two Princeton seniors'
amazing discovery

CALLANAN, LIAM
The Cloud Atlas
Delacorte
Finding love and beauty in
WWII Alaska

COOK, LORNA J.
Departures
St. Martin's
Leaving home for
independent lives

CRAIG, PETER
Hot Plastic
Hyperion
Kevin, following his con-man
dad's path

DANTICAT, EDWIDGE
The Dew Breaker
Knopf
The torturer's daughter,
unraveling secrets

DAVIS, AMANDA
Wonder When You'll Miss Me
William Morrow
Leaving violence to join
the circus

DAY, CATHY
The Circus in Winter
Harcourt
Tragedy, love and loss for
3 generations

FALCONER, HELEN
Sky High
Persea
Music, sex, and parent problems

FISHCHER, JACKIE MOYER
An Egg on Three Sticks
Thomas Dunne
First love shadowed by
mental illness

FROMM, PETE
As Cool As I Am
Picador
Lucy and Kenny overwhelmed
by sex

GILLISON, SAMANTHA
The King of America
Random House
Lost at sea exploring New Guinea

HADDON, MARK
The Curious Incident of the Dog in the Night-Time
Doubleday
An autistic boy playing Sherlock

HALPIN, BRENDAN
Donorboy
Random House
Sudden fatherhood for a
sperm donor

HALLOWELL, JANIS
The Annunciation of Francesca Dunn
William Morrow
Normal teen or divine being?

HARUF, KENT
Eventide
Knopf
Painful and blessed lives
in a small town

HOFFMAN, ALICE
Blackbird House
Doubleday
200 years of love and loss

HYLAND, M. J.
How the Light Gets In
Canongate
An unhappy exchange
student in Chicago

JUST, WARD
An Unfinished Season
Houghton Mifflin
Wilson, 19, falling in love

KRYGIER, LEORA
When She Sleeps
Toby
Half-sisters, Vietnamese
and American

LANGER, ADAM
Crossing California
Riverhead
Chicago teens seeking
love and laughter

The Work of Wolves

BY KENT MEYERS
Harcourt, 2004

Earl closed the calculus book. Careful: that should be his name. Careful Walks Alone. Who else in the senior class, Indian or white, was doing homework on a Friday night? And not even homework he had to do, but extra work because he felt like it. He picked up the book, stuffed the calculator into its case, stood, walked into the living room and past his mother without looking at her. He kept his face impassive. In his bedroom he found a nylon windbreaker, shrugged into it, slipped on Nikes. The wind gusted harder. His mother brushed her long, dark hair every night, but sometimes Earl wanted to ask her why. What was the point? Who was she brushing it for? He knew: his father. Cyrus Walks Alone. Earl knew roads could have sudden endings. He knew if light grew bright enough it could be the hardest thing in the world. But he wanted to tell his mother, sometimes, not to be so careful. And not to expect it so much from him. As far as Earl knew, his father had been careful. What good had it done him?

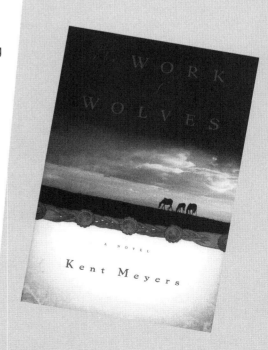

LLOYD, DAVID
*Boys
Syracuse Univ.
Rowdy, friendly, shocking, and real

MENO, JOE
*Hairstyles of the Damned
Akashic/Punk Planet
Brian, falling for a tough punk rocker

MEYERS, KENT
*The Work of Wolves
Harcourt
Earl and Willi rescuing abused horses

NICHOLLS, DAVID
*A Question of Attraction
Villard
First year in college, UK style

PACKER, ZZ
Drinking Coffee Elsewhere
Riverhead
Black youth, eight stories with a twist

PARKS, SUZAN-LORI
Getting Mother's Body
Random House
Pregnant Billy, 16, robbing a grave

PHILLIPS, DELORES
*The Darkest Child
Soho
Choosing school over prostitution

PICOULT, JODI
*My Sister's Keeper
Atria
Anna, questioning her role as a donor

PORTER, CONNIE
Imani All Mine
Mariner
Tasha, 15, and now a mother

ROTH, PHILIP
*The Plot Against America
Houghton Mifflin
A Nazi sympathizer as president

SAPPHIRE
Push
Vintage
Precious, an abused survivor, speaks

SHEPARD, JIM
*Project X
Knopf
Two eighth-grade loners taking revenge

SHREVE, ANITA
*Light on Snow
Little, Brown
Finding an abandoned baby in the woods

SLOAN, KAY
*The Patron Saint of Red Chevys
Permanent
Teen age girls looking for a mother's killer

SULLIVAN, MARY
*Ship Sooner
William Morrow
Suffering because of her keen hearing

TOEWS, MIRIAM
*A Complicated Kindness
Counterpoint
Nomi, longing to leave a Mennonite town

WARD, LIZA
*Outside Valentine
Henry Holt
Teens on a killing spree

WATT, ALAN
Diamond Dogs
Little, Brown
Star quarterback, covering up a crime

Rap, Rock and Bach

BASTFIELD, DARRIN KEITH
Back in the Day
Ballantine
Life and times with Tupac Shakur

BOZZA, ANTHONY
Whatever You Say I Am
Crown
The life and times of Eminem

BRANT, MARLEY
*Tales From the Rock 'N' Roll Highway
Watson-Guptill
The fun and the troubles

CHAPMAN, RICHARD
Guitar
DK
From Segovia to Clapton

CHIRAZI, STEFFAN, EDITOR
*So What!
Broadway
Metallica, the official chronicle

COOPER, MARTHA
*Hip Hop Files
From Here to Fame
Documenting the movement—1979–1984

DEROGATIS, JIM AND CARMÉL CARRILLO, EDITORS
*Kill Your Idols
Barricade
Criticizing classic rock

GETZINGER, DONNA AND DANIEL FELSENFELD
*Johann Sebastian Bach
Morgan Reynolds
A life in music

HARTOCOLLIS, ANEMONA
*Seven Days of Possibilities
PublicAffairs
Bronx kids singing gospel in Finland

HART, MICKEY WITH KOSTYAL
Song Catchers
National Geographic
In search of the world's music

HOROWITZ, JOSEPH
Dvořák in America
Cricket
The Czech composer's U.S. visit

HOYE, JACOB AND KAROLYN ALI, EDITORS
Tupac: Resurrection 1971–1996
Atria
Still life in words and pictures

KEYS, ALICIA
*Tears for Water
Putnam's
Opening her heart in verse

KONOW, DAVID
Bang Your Head
Three Rivers
Rise and fall of heavy metal

LIGHT, ALAN, EDITOR
Vibe History of Hip Hop
Three Rivers
Old School to the end of the century

MALONE, BONZ; NICOLE BATTLE AND DJ LINDY
Hip Hop Immortals
Thunder's Mouth
Photographers capturing entertainers

PARTRIDGE, ELIZABETH
This Land Was Made for You and Me
Viking
The life and songs of Woody Guthrie

RODRIGUEZ-DUARTE, ALEXIS
*Presenting Celia Cruz
Clarkson Potter
The Cuban born Queen of Salsa

SCRIMGEOUR, DIANA
*U2 Show
Riverhead
Twenty-five years on tour

SLICHTER, JACOB
*So You Wanna be a Rock & Roll Star
Broadway
A look at the business of pop music

SUMMERS, JODI
Moving up in the Music Business
Allworth
Plan for success

WARD, GEOFFREY C. AND KEN BURNS
Jazz
Knopf
A history of America's music

Historical Fiction

ANDERSON, LAURIE HALSE
Fever 1793
Simon & Schuster
Enduring the deadly epidemic

ATTEMA, MARTHA
When the War is Over
Orca
Janke, fighting Germans, loving a German

AVI
Crispin
Hyperion
Taking a new name, fleeing his enemies

BYRD, MAX
***Shooting the Sun**
Bantam
To capture an eclipse with daguerreotype

CEELY, JONATHA
***Mina**
Delacorte
Hiding her past in a British kitchen

CHIPMAN, LIZ
***From the Lighthouse**
Dutton
Weezie after her mother left in 1938

CRIST-EVANS, CRAIG
Amaryllis
Candlewick
Two brothers separated by war

CROWE, CHRIS
Mississippi Trial
Phyllis Fogelman
The summer Emmett Till was murdered

DONNELLY, JENNIFER
A Northern Light
Harcourt
A girl's dreams disturbed by murder

DURBIN, WILLIAM
***The Darkest Evening**
Orchard
Fleeing a Communist Finnish utopia

HARRIS, ROBERT
Pompeii
Random House
When Vesuvius erupted

HASSINGER, PETER W.
***Shakespeare's Daughter**
Laura Geringer
Who wanted to be a singer

HAUSMAN, GERALD AND LORETTA HAUSMAN
Escape from Botany Bay
Orchard
Mary, 19 sent to Australia in chains

HESSE, KAREN
Witness
Scholastic
When the Ku Klux Klan comes to Vermont

HOLM, JENNIFER L.
***Boston Jane: The Claim**
HarperCollins
Frontier trials for an independent girl

HOLMES, VICTORIA
***Rider in the Dark**
HarperCollins
Helena's dangerous night rides

LAWRENCE, IAIN
***B for Buster**
Delacorte
16 and flying bombing raids over Germany

MCCAUGHREAN, GERALDINE
Stop the Train
HarperCollins
Building a new Oklahoma town

MORGAN, ROBERT
Brave Enemies
Algonquin
Josie, disguised as a man in the 1780s

RABIN, STATON
***Betsy and the Emperor**
Margaret K. McElderry
A young friend of the captured Napoleon

REES, CELIA
Pirates!
Bloomsbury
Girls seeking treasure and freedom

TETZNER, LISA AND HANNES BINDER
***The Black Brothers**
Front Street
Sold to be a chimneysweep

UPDALE, ELEANOR
***Montmorency: Thief, Liar, Gentleman?**
Orchard
Master and servant in one body

*new book title

Montmorency: Thief, Liar, Gentleman?

BY ELEANOR UPDALE
Orchard Books, 2004

It was only much later, on that chilly morning in the prison hospital, that Montmorency realized how great a gift Sir Joseph Bazalgette had delivered. The map of the sewers, now imprinted on his mind because of his humiliation on the stage, could be the guide to his future career of crime. The tunnels were a new and secret route around London, serving, indeed, the richest areas, where the most profitable thieving could be done.

He lay there constructing a series of fantasy raids: seeing himself emerging from a hole in the ground, smashing, grabbing, and disappearing again as his victims and the flat-footed police ran around above his head frantically seeking the robber. He could almost feel the diamonds in his hand as he staged and restaged each crime. He wasn't stupid. He knew there would be difficulties. In fact, the more he thought about the plan, the more difficulties he foresaw. But Montmorency knew that, locked up in prison, he had time, and he resolved to dedicate the years until his release to solving those problems, and to devising the perfect method for getting as rich as the men who had giggled at him at the Scientific Society. This was going to be something far bigger than the petty thieving that had filled his life since childhood. But it needed to be worked out to the tiniest detail....

science

Brain Food

BRYSON, BILL
A Short History of Nearly Everything
Broadway
And how we know what we know

CARLSON, DALE
In and Out of Your Mind
Bick
How science applies to your life

CURTIS, BRYAN, EDITOR
***The Explainer**
Anchor
Questions we never think to ask

DAVIS, L. J.
Fleet Fire
Arcade
Inventors harnessing electricity

FALK, DAN
***Universe on a T-Shirt**
Arcade
Searching for the Holy Grail of physics

FELDMAN, DAVID
***Do Elephants Jump?**
HarperCollins
Do skunks think skunks stink and more

FLANNERY, SARAH WITH DAVID FLANNERY
In Code
Algonquin
A teen's prize-winning cryptography work

GEE, HENRY
***The Science of Middle-Earth**
Cold Spring
Knowledge that enriches a fantasy classic

GOTT, J. RICHARD, III
Time Travel in Einstein's Universe
Houghton Mifflin
From science fiction to science fact?

JARGODZKI, CHRISTOPHER
Mad About Physics
Wiley
Brain twisters, paradoxes, and curiosities

JORDAN, MICHAEL
Hush Hush
Firefly
Notorious cases of scientific secrecy

KERROD, ROBIN AND DR. SHARON ANN HOLGATE
The Way Science Works
DK
Experiments that explain our world

LE COURTEUR, PENNY & JAY BURRESON
Napoleon's Buttons
Jeremy P. Tarcher/Putnam
How history turns on atomic structure

MASOFF, JOY
Oh, Yuck!
Workman
Why snot is hot and pus is a must

MCCLAFFERTY, CARLA KILLOUGH
The Head Bone's Connected to the Neck Bone
Farrar, Straus and Giroux
The history and mystery of x-rays

OLSON, STEVE
***Count Down**
Houghton Mifflin
Teens take the world's hardest math test

PATENT, DOROTHY HINSHAW
Charles Darwin
Holiday House
One of the inventors of modern science

PRESTON, RICHARD
The Demon in the Freezer
Random House
Studying smallpox to defeat terrorists

RATHJEN, DON
Square Wheels
Exploratorium
31 projects that make science fun

REEVES, DIANE LINDSEY
Career Ideas for Kids Who Like Math
Facts on File
From actuary to urban planner

RIDLEY, MATT
Nature Via Nurture
HarperCollins
Exploring the roots of human behavior

ROBBINS, LOUISE E.
Louis Pasteur
Oxford Univ. Pr.
Who changed the way we fight disease

SACKS, OLIVER
Uncle Tungsten
Knopf
Memories of a chemical boyhood

SILVERSTEIN, ALVIN, VIRGINIA SILVERSTEIN AND LAURA SILVERSTEIN NUNN
DNA
Twenty-First Century
Revealing the code of life

SILVERSTEIN, KEN
***The Radioactive Boy Scout**
Random House
Building a backyard breeder reactor

The Universe and Beyond

ACKROYD, PETER
***Escape from Earth**
DK
Our journey into space

BOERST, WILLIAM J.
Johannes Kepler
Morgan Reynolds
Discovered the laws of celestial motion

CHAIKIN, ANDREW
***Space**
Firefly
Photos from The Final Frontier

DUPAS, ALAIN
***Destination Mars**
Firefly
The call of the red planet

JACKSON, ELLEN
Looking for Life in the Universe
Houghton Mifflin
Scientists who look for E.T.s

KERROD, ROBIN
Hubble
Firefly
Amazing images from
deep space
Universe
DK
Vast space and all that it holds

MACKENZIE, DANA
The Big Splat,
or How Our Moon
Came to Be
Wiley
The birth of our celestial neighbor

TYSON, NEIL DE GRASSE,
CHARLES LIU &
ROBERT IRION
One Universe
Joseph Henry
Finding a connection to the cosmos

VANCLEAVE, JANICE
Janice VanCleave's A+
Projects in Astronomy
Wiley
Out of this world experiments

Fur, Feathers and Scales

ATTENBOROUGH, DAVID
The Life of Mammals
Princeton Univ. Press
From the pygmy shrew to the
blue whale

CARWARDINE, MARK
*Shark
Firefly
Man-killer or endangered specie

CHALMERS, CATHERINE
*American Cockroach
Aperture
Our revulsion revisited

DIBSIE, PATRICIA
Love Heels
Yorkville
Canine companions making
life easier

GREEN-ARMYTAGE,
STEPHEN
Extraordinary Pigeons
Abrams
Not your typical statue sitters

HALE, RACHAEL
*101 Cataclysms
Bulfinch
A celebration of our feline friends
101 Salivations
Bulfinch
A tribute in photos to our pet dogs

HEARNE, BETSY
The Canine Connection
Margaret K. McElderry
Stories about that special
relationship

HODGKINS, FRAN
Animals Among Us
Linnet
When wildlife moves to
the suburbs

IVERSEN, EVE
Animal Aviators
Watts
Flying, gliding, darting, soaring

KARR, KATHLEEN
*Exiled
Marshall Cavendish
A camel's life in Texas

KATZ, JON
*The Dogs of
Bedlam Farm
Villard
Writer turned sheepherder
and his dogs

KRÜGER, KOBIE
The Wilderness Family
Ballantine
Seventeen years with
African wildlife

LACRAMPE, CORINE
Sleep and Rest
in Animals
Firefly
Do insects sleep?
Do reptiles dream?

MILLS, STEPHEN
*Tiger
Firefly
Supple, powerful, long,
lean, intense

MONTGOMERY, SY
*Search for the
Golden Moon Bear
Houghton Mifflin
Amazing animals in the
Asian jungles

MORTON, ALEXANDRA
Listening to Whales
Ballantine
A life spent studying orcas

MURPHY, CLAIRE RUDOLF
AND JANE G. HAIGH
Gold Rush Dogs
Alaska Northwest
Balto, Yukon, Togo and
other canine heroes

RUSSON, ANNE E.
Orangutans
Firefly
Smart, cute and man's
closest relation

SCHAFER, KEVIN
Penguin Planet
NorthWord
Comic on land, but so
graceful in the sea

STANTON, BILL
The Tao of Maggie
Andrews McMeel
Life lessons from a
Basset hound

TAYLOR, THEODORE
Lord of the Kill
Blue Sky
Ben, 16, must rescue a
kidnapped tiger

THAYER, HELEN
*Three Among
the Wolves
Sasquatch
One dog, two humans,
three wolf packs

THOMAS,
ELIZABETH
MARSHALL
The Social
Lives of Dogs
Pocket
How they relate
in their world
and ours

WALKER,
SALLY M.
Fossil Fish
Found Alive
Carolrhoda
Discovering the
Coelacanth

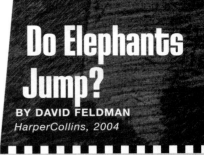

Do Elephants Jump?

BY DAVID FELDMAN
HarperCollins, 2004

Why Do We Say "P.U." When
Something Smells Awful?

We were wondering if the etymology dates back to one Pépé le Pew's debut on the silver screen. Perhaps the spray of a real skunk motivated the first exclamation of "P.U.," but a trip to any dictionary will confirm that this expression of displeasure long predated animated cartoons. Somewhat to our surprise, P.U. is not an abbreviation and not an acronym.

In Latin, the word *puteo* means "to stink, be redolent, or smell bad." The Indo-European word *pu* refers to rot or decay, and many other languages contain words referring to bad smells that start with the letters *pu*. The English interjection *phew* refers to "a vocal gesture expressing impatience, disgust, discomfort, or weariness" according to the *Oxford English Dictionary*, and variants abound (*pew, pho, pheut, phoo, phugh, peugh,* and *fogh,* dating back as far as the early seventeenth century).

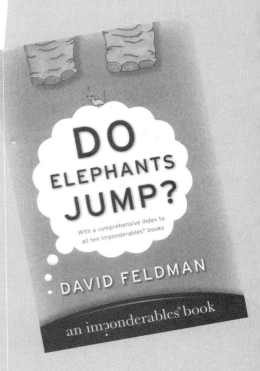

Destination Mars

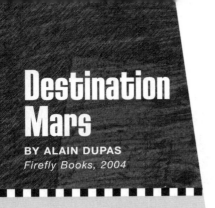

BY ALAIN DUPAS
Firefly Books, 2004

Just a small blood-red spot in the night sky, Mars is not the most spectacular object in the heavens. The Moon shines with an incomparable brightness, and two other planets, Venus and Jupiter, can be brighter. But Mars has indirectly presided over the development of humanity into a scientific and technological civilization during the last few millennia. Aside from the Sun and Moon, no other heavenly object has been as important as Mars in the history of humanity.

Mars may hold the answer to a fundamental question asked by science: Has life appeared anywhere other than on Earth? Throughout time, people have dreamed of conquest. Today, space exploration offers it to them. If the expansion of humanity is to occur beyond planet Earth, it will likely start with Mars, which could become a second Earth, another planet where men, women and children could settle, work and live.

This book is a voyage in space and time; it is fiction based on the latest scientific facts. It invites you for a voyage on the Tsiolkovski, an imaginary craft in the year 2030, with a crew of astronauts on board.

WINN, MARIE
Red-Tails In Love
Pantheon
Hawks and other secrets of Central Park

ZHI, LÜ
Giant Pandas in the Wild
Aperture
Studying and saving an endangered species

Mind and Body

BRYNIE, FAITH HICKMAN
101 Questions About Food and Digestion That Have Been Eating at You... Until Now
Twenty-First Century
Why you really are what you eat

DAVIDSON, SUE AND BEN MORGAN
Human Body Revealed
DK
An illustrated journey through your body

FLEISCHMAN, JOHN
Phineas Gage
Houghton Mifflin
A gruesome advance in brain science

FRIEDLANDER, MARK P., JR.
Outbreak
Lerner
Disease detectives at work

HYMAN, BRUCE M., PH.D. AND CHERRY PEDRICH, R. N.
Obsessive-Compulsive Disorder
Twenty-First Century
Causes, symptoms and current treatment

KENT, DEBORAH
Snake Pits, Talking Cures, & Magic Bullets
Twenty-First Century
A history of mental illness

MARRIOTT, EDWARD
Plague
Metropolitan Books
A threat as long as rats have fleas

MURPHY, WENDY
Spare Parts
Twenty-First Century
From peg legs to gene splices

NILSSON, LENNART AND LARS HAMBERGER
*A Child is Born, 4th edition
Delacorte
The miracle of human reproduction

OFRI, DANIELLE
Singular Intimacies
Beacon
Being a doctor at Bellevue

ROACH, MARY
Stiff
Norton
The curious lives of human cadavers

SILVERSTEIN, ALVIN, VIRGINIA SILVERSTEIN AND LAURA SILVERSTEIN NUNN
Cells
Twenty-First Century
The basic units of life

SLOAN, CHRISTOPHER
Bury the Dead
National Geographic
What the customs of death reveal about us

TRANSUE, EMILY R.
*On Call
St. Martin's
Patients help educate a new doctor

VOGEL, CAROLE GARBUNY
Breast Cancer
Twenty-First Century
What young women need to know

WALKER, RICHARD
Encyclopedia of the Human Body
DK
Colorful guide to all our working parts

WARD, BRIAN
Epidemic
DK
How diseases spread and how we fight them

WERTH, BARRY
From Conception to Birth
Doubleday
Amazing views of human development

Planet Earth

ARTHUS-BERTHRAND, YANN
Earth From Above: 365 Days
Abrams
Portraits of natural and man-made beauty

BANG, MOLLY
Nobody Particular
Holt
One woman's fight to save the Texas Bays

DOHERTY, KIERAN
Marjory Stoneman Douglas
Twenty-First Century
Protector of the Everglades

GAUTHIER, GAIL
Saving the Planet and Stuff
Putnam's
A summer job, a crusade for Michael

HALPERN, SUE
Four Wings and a Prayer
Vintage
Amazing migration of Monarch butterflies

HILL, JULIA BUTTERFLY
One Makes the Difference
HarperSanFrancisco
Small changes you make save the earth

HUGHES, MEREDITH SAYLES
Yes, We Have Bananas
Lerner
And other fruits from shrubs and vines

LEUZZI, LINDA
Life Connections
Watts
Pioneers in ecology

LYNCH, JOHN
The Weather
Firefly
Windy, wet, hot, cold and changing

MATTHEWS, ANNE
Wild Nights
North Point
Nature returns to the Big Apple

PATENT, DOROTHY HINSHAW
Shaping the Earth
Houghton Mifflin
Forces that formed our planet

PRINGLE, LAURENCE
The Environmental Movement
HarperCollins
Grassroots beginnings to global awareness

RENSHAW, AMANDA
Heaven & Earth
Phaidon
Worlds unseen by the naked eye

RYDEN, HOPE
Wildflowers Around the Year
Clarion
Skunk Cabbage to New York Ironweed

ST. ANTOINE, SARA
Stories from Where We Live
Milkweed
A celebration of the American prairie

ZEAMAN, JOHN
Overpopulation
Watts
A dangerous trend to ignore

The Way Things Work

ACZEL, AMIR D.
The Riddle of the Compass
Harvest
Who invented it?

BRAIN, MARSHALL
Marshall Brain's More How Stuff Works
Wiley
From espresso machines to fusion bombs

HAMPTON, WILBORN
Meltdown
Candlewick
Eye-witness account of Three Mile Island

KETTLEWELL, CAROLINE
***Electric Dreams**
Carroll & Graf
Teens build a car of the future

KUSHNER, DAVID
Masters of Doom
Random House
Geek geniuses who transformed video games

LEVY, JOEL
Really Useful
Firefly
History of the "stuff" of modern life

OWEN, DAVID
***Copies in Seconds**
Simon & Schuster
Inventing the Xerox machine

Ancient Stones and Bones

BAHN, PAUL G.
Written in Bones
Firefly
Secrets of our distant past revealed

BURNIE, DAVID
***The Concise Dinosaur Encyclopedia**
Kingfisher
From the beginning to the age of mammals

FARLOW, JAMES O.
Bringing Dinosaur Bones to Life
Watts
How we know what we know about dinosaurs

GREENE, MEG
Buttons, Bones, and the Organ Grinder's Monkey
Linnet
Time detectives researching America's past

HAWASS, ZAHI
***Curse of the Pharaohs**
National Geographic
Adventures of an Egyptologist

JACKSON, KEVIN AND JONATHAN STAMP
Building the Great Pyramid
Firefly
Everything we know about an ancient wonder

NOTHDURFT, WILLIAM WITH JOSH SMITH
The Lost Dinosaurs of Egypt
Random House
Bombed in WWII, can new fossils be found?

OBREGÓN, MAURICIO
Beyond the Edge of the Sea
Modern Library
Real voyages remembered now in myth

STANLEY, DIANE
A Time Apart
Trophy
A Texas teen in an Iron Age community

TURNER, ALAN AND MARICIO ANTÓN
***National Geographic Prehistoric Mammals**
National Geographic
They ruled after the dinosaurs

WILCOX, CHARLOTTE
Mummies, Bones, & Body Parts
Carolrhoda
Human remains shed light on many cultures

*new book title

Here and Now

AIDS

BAXTER, DANIEL J.
The Least of These My Brethren
Harcourt Brace
Stories from a NYC AIDS ward doctor

BROADBENT, PATRICIA AND HYDEIA BROADBENT
You Can Get Past the Tears
Villard
Hydeia, 16, defying death with her family

CHECK, WILLIAM A.
AIDS
Chelsea House
Its deadly history and current treatment

NASDIJJ
The Boy and the Dog Are Sleeping
Ballantine
Awee, adopting a father to care for him

STONE, ELIZABETH
A Boy I Once Knew
Algonquin
Vince, teaching about life, after he dies

WHITE, RYAN AND ANN MARIE CUNNINGHAM
Ryan White: My Own Story
Signet
A teen's courageous life with AIDS

WINICK, JUDD
Pedro and Me
Holt
Friendship, loss and The Real World

Do You Believe?

COBBAN, HELENA
The Moral Architecture of World Peace
Univ. Pr. of Virginia
Conversations with 8 Nobel Laureates

DALAI LAMA XIV
Ethics for the New Millennium
Riverhead
Finding happiness in a complex world

GASKINS, PEARL
***I Believe In...**
Cricket
Faith: Christian, Jewish, and Muslim teens

KIMMEL, ERIC A.
Bar Mitzvah
Viking
How a Jewish boy becomes a man

MACK, STAN
The Story of the Jews
Jewish Lights
4,000 years in cartoons

MCCAIN, JOHN WITH MARK SALTER
***Why Courage Matters**
Random House
Finding the strength within yourself

MYERS, WALTER DEAN
A Time to Love
Scholastic
Faith tested beyond the ordinary

OLIVER, MARILYN TOWER
Muhammad
Lucent
The founder of Islam

PHILIP, NEIL
***Mythology of the World**
Kingfisher
Stories of civilizations, gods and heroes

RIESS, JANA
***What Would Buffy Do?**
Wiley
Leading viewers down spiritual paths

SIMONS, GARY, COMPILER
Be the Dream
Algonquin
Immigrants, inner-city youth, prep schools

STREISSGUTH, THOMAS
Utopian Visionaries
Oliver
Trying to create a perfect society

TEZUKA, OSAMU
***Buddha: Volume 2, The Four Encounters**
Vertical
More from the life of Siddhartha

WINSTON, DIANA
Wide Awake
Perigee
A Buddhist guide for teens

ZEITLIN, STEVE
The Four Corners of the Sky
Henry Holt
Ancient stories of how the world came to be

The Power of Words

BROOKS, TERRY
Sometimes the Magic Works
Del Rey
Inspiration from a master

CRAIG, STEVE
Sports Writing
Discover Writing
The game plan for a great article

FRANCO, BETSY, EDITOR
Things I Have to Tell You
Candlewick
Poems and writing by teenage girls

FRANK, STEVEN
The Pen Commandments
Pantheon
Unbreakable rules for better writing

JACKMAN, IAN, EDITOR
***The Writer's Mentor**
Random House
Advice from the world-famous writers

JACOB, IRIS
My Sisters' Voices
Holt
Teenage girls of color speak out

JONES, CAROLYN
Every Girl Tells a Story
Simon & Schuster
About her life, dreams, future

KEHRET, PEG
Five Pages a Day
Albert Whitman & Co.
Adventure, travel and a writer's journey

LEVITHAN, DAVID, EDITOR
You Are Here This is Now
Scholastic
Poems, stories, essays and art by teens

MIRRIAM-GOLDBERG, CARYN
Write Where You Are
Free Spirit
Making sense of your life

MORRISON, LILLIAN, COMPILER
It Rained All Day That Night
August House
Sign the album with a rhyme

NIXON, JOAN LOWERY
The Making of a Writer
Delacorte
An author of mysteries shares tips

QUINION, MICHAEL
***Ballyhoo, Buckaroo, and Spuds**
Smithsonian
Funny stories behind strange words

SAYLOR, SARA, EDITOR
***The Best Teen Writing of 2004**
Alliance for Young Artists and Writers, Inc.
A nation's award-winning voices

SULLIVAN, HELEN AND LINDA SERNOFF
Research Reports
Millbrook
Interviews, print and on-line sources

WAGMAN, CAT
Why...Thank You!
Working Words
The when and how of note writing

Drugs

BAYER, LINDA N.
Drugs, Crime, and Criminal Justice
Chelsea House
Past and present

BURGESS, MELVIN
Smack
Henry Holt
Gemma and Tar in love— with heroin

CHERIPKO, JAN
Imitate the Tiger
Boyds Mills
Alcohol threatens Chris's football career

CHILDRESS, ALICE
A Hero Ain't Nothin' but a Sandwich
Puffin
13-year-old Benjie's struggle with heroin

CORSER, KIRA AND FRANCES PAYNE ADLER
When the Bough Breaks
New Sage
Addiction plus pregnancy equals tragedy

GANTOS, JACK
Hole in My Life
Farrar, Straus and Giroux
A famous author's prison experiences

GOTTFRIED, TED
Should Drugs Be Legalized?
Twenty-First Century
Pro and con

HOPKINS, ELLEN
***Crank**
Simon Pulse
Kristina becoming Bree; bold and addicted

HYDE, MARGARET O. AND JOHN SETARO, M.D.
Drugs 101
Twenty-First Century
Consequences, current controversy, crime

KUHN, CYNTHIA, SCOTT SWARTZWELDER AND WILKIE WILSON
***Buzzed,**
revised edition
Norton
The straight facts: alcohol, ecstasy, more

TAYLOR, CLARK
The House that Crack Built
Chronicle
Numbing the pain, killing the brain

TULLSON, DIANE
***Blue Highway**
Fitzhenry & Whiteside
Alcohol and Ryan between best friends

I Believe In...
BY PEARL GASKINS
Cricket Books, 2004

"We have reason to believe that religion and spirituality are very significant matters in the lives of many American teenagers," states Smith. More than eighty percent of American teenagers hold some religious affiliation, according to the study. Researchers also found the following to be true about American teens:

- About 35 percent say they attend religious services weekly, and another 15 percent attend at least monthly.

- About 30 percent say that religious faith is extremely important in their lives, and another 30 percent say religious faith is somewhat important in their lives.

- About 40 percent report that they pray daily.

- About 40 percent have participated in a religious youth group for two years or more.

- About 25 percent say that they have been "born again."

These statistics show that a large number of American youth are religious and that many practice their faith. That's not surprising, since religion — its practices, belief systems, and institutions — is a powerful force in our world.

I Believe In ...
Christian, Jewish, and Muslim Young People Speak About Their Faith
Pearl Gaskins

Getting it Together

ABRAHAMS, GEORGE, PH.D AND SHEILA AHLBRAND
Boy v. Girl?
Free Spirit
Nature, nurture or no difference?

BARRY, DOUGLAS
*Wisdom for a Young CEO
Running Press
Business ethics and advice from the top

BLOCK, JOEL D., DR. AND DR. SUSAN S. BARTELL
Step Living For Teens
PSS
The new family-both hope and heartache

BOYERS, SARA JANE
Teen Power Politics
Twenty-First Century
Your voice, your vote

CADIER, FLORENCE WITH MELISSA DALY
*My Parents are Getting Divorced
Amulet
Survival tactics for the whole family

CHIN, BEVERLY ANN, SERIES CONSULTANT
*How to Study for Success
Wiley
Simple steps to better grades

FROST, HELEN
Keesha's House
Farrar, Straus and Giroux
Sheltering the lost kids

GASKINS, PEARL FUYO
What Are You?
Henry Holt
Voices of mixed-race youth

THE GIRLSOURCE EDITORIAL TEAM
GirlSource
Ten Speed
For girls, by girls with attitude

HALL, COLIN AND RON LIEBER
Taking Time Off,
updated second edition
Princeton Review
Success beyond school

HALPIN, MIKKI
*It's Your World— If You Don't Like It, Change It
Simon Pulse
Being an activist in your own community

HERNANDEZ, MICHELLE A.
Acing the College Application
Ballantine
How to get in

HYDE, MARGARET O. AND ELIZABETH H. FOSYTH M.D.
Depression
Watts
History, hypothesies, help

IISENBERG, MARC
The Student Athlete Survival Guide
McGraw Hill
Have it all: sports, grades, social life

LE JEUNE, VERONIQUE, PHILIPPE ELIAKIM WITH MELISSA DALY
*Feeling Freakish?
Amulet
Your body as a work in progress

MARRINER, MIKE; NATHAN GEBHARD WITH JOANNE GORDON
Roadtrip Nation
Ballantine
12 cities, 30 jobs, one trip

MCGOWAN, EILEEN NIXON AND NANCY LAGOW DUMAS
Stock Market Smart
Millbrook
Investing for beginners

MCGRAW, JAY
The Ultimate Weight Solution for Teens
Free Press
Sensible advice from Dr. Phil's son

MOKA WITH MELISSA DALY
*Just Us Girls
Amulet
Secrets to feeling good about yourself

MORGENSTERN, JULIE AND JESSI MORGENSTERN-COLON
Organizing From the Inside Out For Teens
Owl
Your room, your time, your life

MUHARRAR, AISHA
More Than a Label
Free Spirit
Not being limited by what peers say

PERRY, CHERYL L., LESLIE LYTLE AND TERESA G. JACOBS
*The Vegetarian Manifesto
Running Press
Get the facts to make the choice

PACKER, ALEX J.
How Rude!
Free Spirit
A humorous guide to good manners

SHANLEY, ELLEN AND COLLEEN THOMPSON
Fueling the Teen Machine
Bull
Stay healthy, eat right

TAN, SHAUN
The Red Tree
Simply Red Books
Bad day becoming not so bad

TRULY, TRACI
Teen Rights
Sphinx
At school, home, work, in your life

Crime and Justice

ABBOTT, GEOFFREY
*The Executioner Always Chops Twice
St. Martin's
Putting criminals to death

ANGELICA, JADE CHRISTINE
We Are Not Alone
Haworth
Incest: disclosure through prosecution

BERGERON, DEB AND PAULA BREWER BYRON, EDITORS
From the Pain Come the Dream
Umbrage
Award-winning activists against injustice

BODE, JANET
Voices of Rape,
revised edition
Watts
Victims and rapists speak

CRAIG, EMILY
*Teasing Secrets Fom the Dead
Crown
Infamous crime scene investigations

GOTTFRIED, TED
Homeland Security Versus Constitutional Rights
Twenty-First Century
Protecting our nation against terrorism

HILLDORFER, JOSEPH AND ROBERT DUGONI
*The Cyanide Canary.
Free Press
Bringing a dangerous polluter to justice

JUNKIN, TIM
*Bloodsworth
Algonquin
First death row inmate exonerated by DNA

KING, MICHAEL R. AND GREGORY M. COOPER WITH DON DENEVI
*Who Killed King Tut?
Prometheus
Modern methods examine an ancient mystery

ORR, TAMRA
Violence In Our Schools
Watts
Halls of hope, halls of fear

RODRÍGUEZ, JOSEPH
*Juvenile
powerHouse
Images of what youthful offenders face

SALZMAN, MARK
True Notebooks
Knopf
Writings about life
from juvenile hall

SHEELER, JACKIE, EDITOR
Off the Cuffs
Soft Skull
Bravery and brutality:
police poems

SPARGO, TAMSIN
*Wanted Man
Bloomsbury
The wild tale of a dashing
train robber

SUTTON, RANDY, COMPILER
*True Blue
St. Martin's
What it means to be a cop

Looking Good

BIRD, EUGENIE
Fairie-ality
Candlewick
An adventure in fashion design

BROWN, BOBBI AND
ANNEMARIE IVERSON
**Bobbi Brown
Teenage Beauty**
Cliff Street
Appreciate what's special
about you

DICKEY, A.
Hair Rules!
Villard
Good hair: kinky, curly, wavy

MASON, LINDA
*Teen Makeup
Watson-Guptill
Looks to match your every mood

MASTALIA, FRANCESCO
AND ALFONSE PAGANO
Dreads
Artisan
A style that spans time
and cultures

MCNAB, NAN
**Body Bizarre
Body Beautiful**
Fireside
Decoration for every age
and color

ODES, REBECCA;
ESTHER DRILL AND
HEATHER MCDONALD
The Looks Book
Penguin
Beauty: why, how and what style

TRAIG, JENNIFER
Crafty Girl: Makeup
Chronicle
Do-it-yourself colors, your style

WARRICK, LEANNE
*Hair Trix for Cool Chix
Watson-Guptill
TLC for all types of hair,
for all girls

Love and Sex

BECKERMAN, MARTY
*Generation S.L.U.T.
MTV Books/Pocket
Statistics, exaggerations, lies
and truth

BODE, JANET
AND STAN MACK
Heartbreak and Roses,
revised edition
Watts
True stories of troubled love

BRYNIE, FAITH HICKMAN
**101 Questions About
Sex and Sexuality**
Twenty-First Century
All the answers you've been
looking for

BURGESS, MELVIN
*Doing It
Henry Holt
The truth behind the
"player's talk"

CLAUSNER-PETIT, MAGALI
WITH MELISSA DALY
*Sex Explained
Amulet
Your guide to the birds and bees

DOMITRZ, MICHAEL J.
*May I Kiss You?
Awareness
When it is okay, and when
it is not

LINDSAY, JEANNE WARREN
Teen Dads,
revised edition
Morning Glory
Supporting your partner and child

MADARAS, LYNDA
**The "What's
Happening to
My Body?" Book
for Boys,**
3rd edition
Newmarket
Answers to
often-embarrassing questions
**The "What's
Happening to My
Body?" Book for
Girls, 3rd edition**
Newmarket
Your transformation to
womanhood

NAIK, ANITA
*Flirtology
Razorbill
Girls, flirting tips to win guys

TOCCI, SALVATORE
**Sexually
Transmitted
Diseases**
Watts
Thorough answers to
every question

YOUNG, CATHY
One Hot Second
Knopf
Stories about desire

LGBTQ: Being Gay

BOOCK, PAULA
**Dare Truth
or Promise**
Houghton Mifflin
2 girls ask: Have you
ever been in love?

DE OLIVEIRA, EDDIE
*Lucky
Push
Bisexual boys both in
love with Emma

Mongo
BY TED BOTHA
Bloomsbury USA, 2004

The street collector you see today could well be a bum or a lunatic, that's true enough, but just as easily a millionaire, a school-teacher, an accountant, a doctor, a housewife. Much of the story about what they collect, and how and why, is passed along orally, like some secret religion. And perhaps because their pastime is still so easily misunderstood — "Ugh, you collect garbage?" is the refrain that usually greets them — it's seldom that they willingly declare themselves.

Only once you have acknowledged that you're a believer too are collectors happy to open up. And when they do, they blossom, like any real collector would, and their stories fascinate. Some of them also have a word for what they find, a word that is suitably playful and vague. It could be French, Chinese, or even African, but it is, quite appropriately, American slang, concocted in New York for any discarded item that is picked up, retrieved, rescued. That word is *mongo*.

The Burn Journals

BY BRENT RUNYON
Alfred A. Knopf, 2004

I try to say something, ask the woman with red hair if my mom is here, but I can't move my mouth, and my throat is dry from all the cold air they're making me breathe. I'm so cold. I wish I had a blanket or a sweater. I guess I do have a blanket, but I'm still so cold. Maybe when we get to the hospital, they'll give me another blanket or a pair of sweatpants. My body hurts, everything everywhere hurts. I close my eyes.

Something's different, I'm outside again. It's windy. No, it's not. I'm in an elevator, I can tell because of the doors and the lights. Who is that woman talking to me? How does she know my name? She looks like that other woman on that TV show I saw.

And now there are even more lights and lots of people wearing masks. They're putting me on a metal table. And it's so cold, it's so cold. And everybody's talking, but nobody's talking to me. Somebody just said my urine is red. I don't want red urine. I want to cry and I want to sleep.

I want to go back.

FRANCIS, BRIAN
*Fruit
MacAdam/Cage
Peter, wondering, "Am I normal?"

KAESER, GIGI
Love Makes a Family
Univ. of Massachusetts Pr.
Looking at changing values

HUEGEL, KELLY
GLBTQ
Free Spirit
Queer and questioning
survival guide

LEVITHAN, DAVID
Boy Meets Boy
Knopf
Boy loses boy, drama ensues,
boy gets boy

LYON, GEORGE ELLA
*Sonny's House of Spies
Simon & Schuster
Digging up family secrets
in Alabama

MASTBAUM, BLAIR
*Clay's Way
Alyson
Desire and pain in Hawaii

MERRELL, BILLY
Talking in the Dark
Push
About love, about life,
about liking boys

MYRACLE, LAUREN
Kissing Kate
Dutton
Lissa realizing she can't
be just friends

PETERS, JULIE ANNE
*Luna
Little, Brown
Liam dreaming of
showing his true self

SANCHEZ, ALEX
*So Hard to Say
Simon & Schuster
Teetering on the brink
of first love

SMITH, ALISON
*Name All the Animals
Scribner
Alison, losing a brother,
finding love

SUMMER, JANE, EDITOR
*Not the Only One
Alyson
Boys and girls: shy, proud
and queer

TRUJILLO, CARLA
What Night Brings
Curbstone
Marci, wishing God would
make her a boy

WYETH, SHARON DENNIS
*Orphea Proud
Delacorte
Discovering herself at the mike

The Changing Scene

ALLISON, ANTHONY
Hear These Voices
Candlewick
Teens facing a future filled
with risk

ALMOND, STEVE
*Candyfreak
Algonquin
The chocolate underbelly
of America

BAMBERGER, MICHAEL
*Wonderland
Atlantic Monthly
Senior year and an over the
top prom

**BARSON, MICHAEL AND
STEVEN HELLER**
Teenage Confidential
Chronicle
Delinquents, rebels and rock
'n' roll

BOTHA, TED
*Mongo
Bloomsbury
Treasures in the trash

**CETRON, MARVIN
AND OWEN DAVIES**
Probable Tomorrows
St. Martin's
Technology transforming
our lives

GARCIA, BOBBITO
**Where'd You
Get Those?**
Testify
Talking about sneakers in NYC

**GRUNITZKY, CLAUDE
WITH TRACE MAGAZINE
CONTRIBUTORS**
*Transculturalism
powerHouse
How the world is coming together

KATZ, JON
Geeks
Broadway
Jesse and Eric,
no longer outsiders

MORRIS, EVAN
*From Altoids to Zima
Fireside
Stories behind famous
brand names

STEWART, GAIL B.
Teen Dropouts
Gale Group
Why they left and how their
lives changed

TAYLOR, LAWRENCE J.
Tunnel Kids
Univ. of Arizona Pr.
Mexican teens on the border
of the USA

Make up Your Mind

LASSIEUR, ALLISON
Abortion
Lucent
A current discussion of
these issues

LEONE, DANIEL
**Physician-Assisted
Suicide**
Greenhaven
Ethical and legal issues

MORAN, MARK AND MARK SCEURMAN
*Weird U.S.
Barnes & Noble
America's legends and best kept secrets

QUART, ALISSA
Branded
Perseus
Teens: manipulated by the media?

SINGER, MARILYN, EDITOR
*Face Relations
Simon & Schuster
Stories of youth embracing diversity

Overcoming Odds

ABEEL, SAMANTHA
My Thirteenth Winter
Orchard
Enduring a math disability

DAVIS, DEBORAH, EDITOR
*You Look Too Young to be a Mom
Perigee
Teen mothers speak out

DENNISON, AMY; ALLIE DENNISON AND DAVID DENNISON
Our Dad Died
Free Spirit
Coping with grief, living with loss

FERRIS, JEAN
Of Sound Mind
Farrar, Straus and Giroux
Theo, the hearing family member

FISHER, ANTWONE QUENTON AND MIM EICHLER RIVAS
Finding Fish
Morrow
An abandoned boy finding himself

KELLER, HELEN
The Story of My Life,
the restored edition
Modern Library
The challenge of being deaf and blind

LOUISE, REGINA
Somebody's Someone
Warner
Looking for her own loving family

MACK, STAN
Janet & Me
Simon & Schuster
Love and loss in "cancerland"

MCCORMICK, PATRICIA
Cut
Front Street
Callie, seeking help through mutilation

MISHLER, WILLIAM
A Measure of Endurance
Knopf
When Steven, 16, lost his arms

MUSGRAVE, SUSAN, EDITOR
*Perfectly Secret
Annick
The hidden lives of seven teen girls

PLEDGE, DEANNA S., PH.D.
When Something Feels Wrong
Free Spirit
How to survive abuse

RUNYON, BRENT
*The Burn Journals
Knopf
14 and attempting suicide

STONE, MIRIAM
At the End of Words
Candlewick
The year her mother was dying

SUMMER, LAURALEE
Learning Joy from Dogs Without Collars
Simon & Schuster
From homeless shelters to Harvard

TRAIG, JENNIFER
*Devil in the Details
Little, Brown
A funny girl compelled to be obsessive

TWOMEY, CATHLEEN
Beachmont Letters
Boyds Mills
Eleanor, scarred by a fire

Remarkable People

APPELT, KATHI
*My Father's Summers
Henry Holt
Coming of age in an imperfect family

BROKAW, TOM
A Long Way From Home
Random House
The broadcaster's youth in South Dakota

CHRISTENSEN, BONNIE, COMPILER
In My Grandmother's House
HarperCollins
Stories of ties that bind

CONLON-MCIVOR, MAURA
*FBI Girl
Warner
Deciphering her father's secrets

Devil in the Details
BY JENNIFER TRAIG
Little, Brown and Company, 2004

My father and I were in the laundry room and we were having a crisis. It was the strangest thing, but I couldn't stop crying. And there were a few other weird things: I was wearing a yarmulke and a nightgown, for one, and then there were my hands, red and raw and wrapped in plastic baggies. My lip was split. There were paper towels under my feet. And weirdest of all, everything I owned seemed to be in the washing machine, whites and colors, clothes and shoes, barrettes and backpacks, all jumbled together. Huh.

"Huh," my father said, examining the Reebok Esprit Hello Kitty stew churning through permanent press. "You want to tell me what happened here?"

Wasn't it obvious? The fumes from the bacon my sister had microwaved for dessert had tainted everything I owned, so now it all had to be washed. But this sort of rational explanation hadn't been going over well with my father lately. I scramble to think of another, turning lies over in my mouth: it was homework, an experiment; it was performance art, a high-concept piece protesting the consumerization of tweens. I glanced up at my father and down at the machine, then dragged my baggied wrist under my nose and exhaled. "I don't know."

Devil in the Details
scenes from an obsessive girlhood
Jennifer Traig

The Bone Woman

BY CLEA KOFF
Random House, 2004

As we uncovered the deeper layers of the grave, the state of the bodies progressed from skeletonized to mummified to simply decomposing. The direct sunlight during our workday sped up decomposition, creating stench and a sense of stillness. As the number of bodies went into the hundreds, there was barely any soil left between them, they were so tightly pressed together. The reduction in the amount of backdirt that had to be removed meant faster exhumation. This was important, because we had no idea how many more bodies lay below: would it be the one thousand we had estimated on the basis of witness reports? The less skeletonized condition also sped up exhumation, because a body could be lifted out almost whole: we no longer had to carefully gather more than two hundred individual bones. However, we were delayed by the way in which the bodies were entangled with each other.

THE BONE WOMAN

A Forensic Anthropologist's Search for Truth in the Mass Graves of Rwanda, Bosnia, Croatia, and Kosovo

CLEA KOFF

CRUTCHER, CHRIS
King of the Mild Frontier
Greenwillow
Growing up to become an author

DONNELLY, MATT
Theodore Roosevelt
Linnet
Strong president, full of contradiction

DUDMAN, MARTHA TOD
***Expecting to Fly**
Simon & Schuster
Surviving the turbulent sixties

FREEDMAN, RUSSELL
***The Voice That Challenged a Nation**
Clarion
Marian Anderson's place in history

GREEN, JOEY
How They Met
Black Dog & Leventhal
Lovers, rivals and partners in crime

GROSS, TERRY
***All I Did Was Ask**
Hyperion
Interviews with talented artists

HASKINS, JIM
Toni Morrison
Twenty-First Century
The Nobel Prize-winning novelist

HURSTON, LUCY ANNE AND THE ESTATE OF ZORA NEALE HURSTON
***Speak, So You Can Speak Again**
Doubleday
Zora Neale Hurston's creative spirit

KAMEN, GLORIA, EDITOR
Heading Out
Bloomsbury
How amazing careers got started

KASHNER, SAM
***When I Was Cool**
HarperCollins
Living among his idols, the Beat poets

MANDELA, NELSON
Mandela
Little, Brown
The great South African leader

MELTZER, MILTON
Edgar Allan Poe
Twenty-First Century
Short, painful life of a literary genius

MYERS, WALTER DEAN
Bad Boy
HarperCollins
A favorite writer's critical Harlem years

PATCHETT, ANN
***Truth & Beauty**
HarperCollins
A powerful friendship between two writers

ROBINSON, SHARON
***Promises to Keep**
Scholastic
How Jackie Robinson changed America

STING
Broken Music
Dial
Autobiography of a pop icon

STRINGER, LEE
***Sleepaway School**
Seven Stories
Surviving racism, abuse and poverty

ZAMPERINI, LOUIS WITH DAVID RENSIN
Devil at My Heels
Morrow
Living through the brutalities of war

War and Peace

AMBROSE, STEPHEN E.
The Good Fight
Atheneum
An introduction to World War II

ARMSTRONG, JENNIFER, EDITOR
Shattered
Knopf
A dozen stories of young people and war

BAGDASARIAN, ADAM
Forgotten Fire
DK Ink/Melanie Kroupa
Surviving the great Armenian holocaust

BASU, JAY
The Stars Can Wait
Picador
Discovering an older brother's secrets

BRADLEY, KIMBERLY BRUBAKER
For Freedom
Delacorte
Suzanne, a spy for the French Resistance

CHAMBERS, AIDAN
Postcards From No Man's Land
Speak
A secret WWII love affair revealed

COLMAN, PENNY
Where the Action Was
Crown
Women war correspondents of WWII

COOPER, MICHAEL L.
Remembering Manzanar
Clarion
Life in a Japanese relocation camp

CRANE, STEPHEN
The Red Badge of Courage
Henry Holt
An inexperienced boy in Civil War combat

EXUM, ANDREW
***This Man's Army**
Gotham
Fighting al-Qaeda in Afghanistan

GOTTFRIED, TED
The Great Fatherland War
Twenty-First Century
The rise and fall of the Soviet Union

HEDIN, ROBERT, EDITOR
*Old Glory
Persea
Heroism and horror of war
in poetry

HERSEY, JOHN
Hiroshima
Knopf
Six who survived the atom bomb

HOBBS, VALERIE
Sonny's War
Farrar, Straus and Giroux
When Cory's brother went
to Vietnam

KELLY, CLARA OLINK
The Flamboya Tree
Random House
Imprisoned on the island of
Java, WWII

KOFF, CLEA
*The Bone Woman
Random House
Searching for truth in
mass graves

LIPSKY, DAVID
Absolutely American
Houghton Mifflin
Four years, the West Point
experience

LOMAX, DON
Vietnam Journal
ibooks
Fighting a senseless war

MAZER, HARRY
A Boy at War
Simon & Schuster
Adam, eyewitness to Pearl
Harbor attack

MCBRIDE, JAMES
Miracle at St. Anna
Riverhead
WWII: The Buffalo Soldiers'
heroism in Italy

MORPURGO, MICHAEL
*Private Peaceful
Scholastic
At 14, following his brother
into battle

MYERS, WALTER DEAN
Patrol
HarperCollins
A poem of a young soldier
in Vietnam

NELSON, PETE
Left for Dead
Delacorte
Teen seeks justice for a
US Navy captain

**THE NEW YORK TIMES,
EDITORS**
A Nation Challenged
Callaway
A visual history of 9/11 and
its aftermath

O'BRIEN, TIM
**The Things They
Carried**
Broadway
Young foot soldiers in the
madness

OTSUKA, JULIE
**When the Emperor
Was Divine**
Knopf
Japanese Americans sent to
a desert camp

REMARQUE, ERICH MARIA
**All Quiet on the
Western Front**
Little, Brown
German soldiers' experiences
in WWI

WHITE, ELLEN EMERSON
**The Journal of Patrick
Seamus Flaherty**
Scholastic
A young marine in Vietnam, 1968

WILLIAMS, BUZZ
*Spare Parts
Gotham
Marine reservist sent to the
Persian Gulf

WULFFSON, DON
Soldier X.
Viking
Fighting in a war he doesn't
believe in

Working

**ALBRECHT, KAT
WITH JANA MURPHY**
***The Lost Pet
Chronicles**
Bloomsbury
K-9 cop turned pet detective

CODELL, ESMÉ RAJI
Educating Esmé
Algonquin
The diary of a teacher's first year

**EBERTS, MARJORIE AND
MARGARET GISLER**
**Careers for Talkative
Types & Others
with the Gift of Gab**
VGM
Do you have a way with words?

ESQUITH, RAFE
There Are No Shortcuts
Pantheon
An award-winning teacher speaks

GORRELL, GENA K.
Catching Fire
Tundra
Firefighting, taming an enemy

GREEN, MELISSA FAY
Last Man Out
Harcourt
Facing death in a Nova Scotia
coal mine

HAINES, LURENE
**The Writer's Guide
to the Business
of Comics**
Watson-Guptill
Tips from industry insiders

KENIG, GRACIELA
**Best Careers for
Bilingual Latinos**
VGM
Are you fluent in Spanish
and English?

**PASTERNAK, CEEL AND
LINDA THORNBURG**
**Cool Careers for
Girls in Engineering**
Impact
Change the world

ROBERTS-DAVIS, TANYA
**We Need to Go
to School**
Groundwood
Nepalese child carpet workers

SCHIFF, NANCY RICA
Odd Jobs
Ten Speed
Working in peculiar occupations

**SCHWAGER, TINA AND
MICHELE SCHUERGER**
Cool Women, Hot Jobs
Free Spirit
Tips for teens

UNGER, ZAC
*Working Fire
Penguin
The making of an accidental
fireman

ZANNOS, SUSAN
Careers in Education
Mitchell Lane
Latinos at work

Never Again: The Holocaust

**BLEIER, INGE JOSEPH
AND DAVID E. GUMPERT**
*Inge
William B. Eerdmans
Her journey through Nazi Europe

CHOTJEWITZ, DAVID
***Daniel Half Human
and the Good Nazi**
Atheneum
Best friends torn apart by
anti-Semitism

CROCI, PASCAL
*Auschwitz
Abrams
Horrors of the camp in a
graphic novel

FRANK, ANNE
**The Diary of a
Young Girl,**
definitive edition
Doubleday
Her innermost feelings from
her hiding place

GESSEN, MASHA
*Ester and Ruzya
Dial
Grandmothers reliving
Russia's history

With Courage and Cloth

BY ANN BAUSUM
National Geographic, 2004

In 1913 Alice Paul helped plan a parade. It wasn't the nation's first demonstration in support of votes for women, and it wasn't the last one. This parade became a turning point, though, in the 72-year struggle for the right of women to vote in the United States.

Alice Paul organized the parade just as a general might plan for battle. Timing was crucial. The event was set for Monday, March 3, the day before the Inauguration of the nation's 28th President, Woodrow Wilson. Alice Paul and her collaborators knew that plenty of people, including the media would be on hand already for that occasion and would see and report about their event. Location was critical, too. They insisted that the parade follow the same prestigious route reserved for the Inaugural procession.

A small army of volunteers helped design floats, recruit bands, and enlist marchers for the event. Organizers wanted so many women to gather from so many places and with such a varied set of credentials that their presence would be overwhelming.

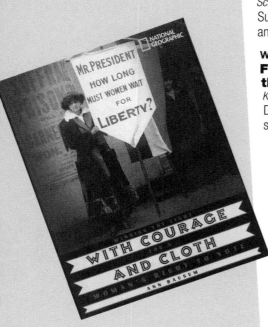

GIBLIN, JAMES CROSS
The Life and Death of Adolf Hitler
Clarion
Portrait of a 20th-century dictator

KOSITSKY, LYNNE
*The Thought of High Windows
Kids Can
Esther's perilous escape route

LEVITIN, SONIA
Room in the Heart
Dutton
Escaping the Nazis in Denmark

NIR, YEHUDA
The Lost Childhood
Scholastic
A Jewish family disguised as Catholic

ROGASKY, BARBARA
Smoke and Ashes, Revised and Expanded Ed.
Holiday House
A history in words and images

SPIEGELMAN, ART
Maus: A Survivor's Tale, I and II
Pantheon
An artist's look at the death camps

STILLMAN, LARRY
A Match Made in Hell
Univ. of Wisconsin
True story: a Jewish boy and an outlaw

WIESEL, ELIE
After the Darkness
Schocken
Surviving the horror and bearing witness

WILSON, JOHN
Flames of the Tiger
Kids Can
Dieter, 17, a German soldier fleeing

Women

BAUSUM, ANN
*With Courage and Cloth
National Geographic
The fight for the right to vote

BOHANNON, LISA FREDERIKSEN
*Woman's Work
Morgan Reynolds
Betty Friedan and women's rights

BOLDEN, TONYA
33 Things Every Girl Should Know About Women's History
Crown
From suffragettes to the E.R.A.

BRODY, MIRIAM
Mary Wollstonecraft
Oxford Univ. Pr.
Mother of Women's Rights

COLMAN, PENNY
Girls
Scholastic
Growing up female in America

COON, NORA E., EDITOR AND COMPILER
It's Your Rite
Beyond Words
Today's girls speak: coming-of-age

DEAK, ERZSI AND KRISTIN EMBRY LITCHMAN, EDITORS
Period Pieces
HarperCollins
Girls on the verge of womanhood

GAINES, ANN
*Coco Chanel
Chelsea House
The revolutionary fashion designer

THE GUERRILLA GIRLS
Bitches, Bimbos, and Ballbreakers
Penguin
A guide to female stereotypes

HARRISON, SABRINA WARD
Brave on the Rocks
Villard
An artist's intimate journey

IHIMAERA, WITI
*The Whale Rider
Harcourt
A Maori girl's sacred gift

KENSCHAFT, LORI
Lydia Maria Child
Oxford University Press
Her quest for racial justice

LABER, JERI
The Courage of Strangers
Public Affairs
Human rights activist's life

LESTER, JOAN STEINAU
Fire in My Soul
Atria
Eleanor Holmes Norton, political pioneer

MAURER, RICHARD
The Wright Sister
Roaring Brook
The woman behind the famous men

NAM, VICKIE
Yell-Oh Girls!
Quill
Asian Americans speaking up

SULLIVAN, OTHA RICHARD
African American Women Scientists & Inventors
Wiley
Black stars present and past

WARD, GEOFFREY C.
Not For Ourselves Alone
Knopf
Elizabeth Cady Stanton & Susan B. Anthony

ZUKERMAN, EUGENIA
In My Mother's Closet
Sorin
Daughters remembering

*new book title

One World

Africa

ADICHIE, CHIMAMANDA NGOZI
Purple Hibiscus
Algonquin
Lives shattered under a miliary coup

BEARD, PETER
***Zara's Tales**
Knopf
Adventures with wildlife in Kenya

DIALLO, KADIATOU AND CRAIG WOLFF
My Heart Will Cross This Ocean
One World
Remembering her son Amadou and more

DIRIE, WARIS
Desert Flower
Ariel
Escaping Somalia's harsh traditions

ELLIS, DEBORAH
***The Heaven Shop**
Fitzhenry & Whiteside
How AIDS devastated Binti's family

EMECHETA, BUCHI
The Bride Price
George Braziller
An Ibo girl's ill-fated love

FARMER, NANCY
A Girl Named Disaster
Orchard
On a harrowing journey to Zimbabwe

FULLER, ALEXANDRA
Don't Let's Go to the Dogs Tonight
Random House
A white family in rural war-torn Rhodesia

KURTZ, JANE, EDITOR
***Memories of Sun**
Amistad/Greenwillow
Stories of growing up African today

LAINÉ, DANIEL AND PIERRE ALEXANDRE
African Kings
Ten Speed
Vivid portraits of tribal royalty

LEKUTON, JOSEPH LEMASOLAI WITH HERMAN VIOLA
Facing the Lion
National Geographic
Growing up Maasai on the Kenyan savanna

MAFUNDIKWA, SAKI
***Afrikan Alphabets**
Mark Batty
Writing systems as culture and art

MANKELL, HENNING
Secrets in the Fire
Annick
Sofia's life in war-torn Mozambique

MATHABANE, MIRIAM AS TOLD TO MARK MATHABANE
Miriam's Song
Simon & Schuster
Growing up oppressed in South Africa

MCCALL SMITH, ALEXANDER
***The Girl Who Married a Lion and Other Tales from Africa**
Pantheon
Folktales from Zimbabwe and Botswana

NAIDOO, BEVERLEY
Out of Bounds
HarperCollins
Seven stories of South African lives

NAZER, MENDE AND DAMIEN LEWIS
***Slave**
PublicAffairs
Seized from her Sudanese village at 12

PATON, ALAN
Cry, the Beloved Country
Scribner's
A Zulu parson in search of his son

REEF, CATHERINE
This Our Dark Country
Clarion
Liberia, its ongoing, troubled history

STRATTON, ALLAN
***Chanda's Secrets**
Annick
Dreams of the future as death takes hold

TADJO, VÉRONIQUE, EDITOR
***Talking Drums**
Bloomsbury
Introducing poems from the continent

The Middle East

CHACHAM, RONIT
Breaking Ranks
Other Press
Conscientious objectors of Israel

GARRELS, ANNE
Naked in Baghdad
Farrar, Straus and Giroux
A journalist views the war in Iraq

GROSSMAN, DAVID
***Someone to Run With**
Farrar, Straus and Giroux
Two lonely teens find love in Jerusalem

HAKAKIAN, ROYA
***Journey from the Land of No**
Crown
Coming of age as revolution sweeps Iran

HOSSEINI, KHALED
The Kite Runner
Riverhead
Amir and Hassan: friends in Kabul

KASS, PNINA MOED
***Real Time**
Clarion
One violent moment on a Jerusalem highway

Burned Alive

BY SOUAD
Warner Books, 2004

I am a girl. A girl must walk fast, head down, as if counting the number of steps she's taking. She may never stray from her path or look up, for if a man were to catch her eye, the whole village would label her a charmuta. If a married neighbor woman, or an old woman, or just anybody were to see her out without her mother or her older sister, without her sheep, her bundle of hay, or her load of figs, they would right away say charmuta. A girl must be married before she can raise her eyes and look straight ahead, or go into a shop, or pluck her eyebrows and wear jewelry. My mother was married at fourteen. If a girl is still unmarried by that age, the village begins to make fun of her. But a girl must wait her turn in the family to be married. The oldest daughter first, then the others.

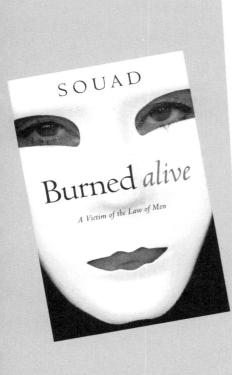

MACAULAY, DAVID
Mosque
Houghton Mifflin
An imaginary 16th century building

NYE, NAOMI SHIHAB
19 Varieties of Gazelle
Greenwillow
Treasured memories of a homeland in poems

SATRAPI, MARJANE
Persepolis
Pantheon
A childhood in Iran: a graphic novel
***Persepolis 2**
Pantheon
A young rebel finding her place

SCHWARTZ, LARRY, EDITOR
The War in Iraq
ReganBooks
Photos of soldiers, civilians, and more

SOUAD
***Burned Alive**
Warner
When a girl breaks the rules in Palestine

Asia

ANSARY, TAMIM
West of Kabul, East of New York
Farrar, Straus and Giroux
Memoir of an Afghan American life

AOKI, SHOICHI
Fruits
Phaidon
Wild-style fashions of Japanese youth

CHEN, DA
Sounds of the River
HarperCollins
From Yellow Stone village to university

DAI, SIJIE
Balzac and the Little Chinese Seamstress
Knopf
2 boys telling tales from forbidden books

ELLIS, DEBORAH
Mud City
Groundwood
Dreams beyond the refugee camp

FREEDMAN, RUSSELL
Confucius
Arthur A. Levine
Philosopher, educator, diplomat

FU, SHELLEY
Ho Yi the Archer and Other Classic Chinese Tales
Linnet
Seven remarkable stories

HAQ, HINA
***Sadika's Way**
Academy Chicago
How tradition rules her life in Pakistan

HOOBLER, DOROTHY AND THOMAS
***In Darkness, Death**
Philomel
On a murderer's trail in 18th c. Japan

KOUL, SUDHA
The Tiger Ladies
Beacon
Memories of Kashmir, a "Paradise on Earth"

LIU, SIYU AND OREL PROTOPOPESCU
A Thousand Peaks
Pacific View
Introducing the poetry of China

MAH, ADELINE YEN
Falling Leaves
Wiley
A childhood without love in China

MAJOR, JOHN AND BETTY J. BELANUS
Caravan to America
Cricket
8 who practice the arts of the Silk Road

MIN, ANCHEE
Wild Ginger
Houghton Mifflin
Two girls in love with the same boy

NAMU, YANG ERCHE AND CHRISTINE MATHIEU
Leaving Mother Lake
Little, Brown
A singer looks back at a Chinese girlhood

NAPOLI, DONNA JO
***Bound**
Atheneum
Xing Xing, a Chinese Cinderella's story

O'CONNOR, JANE
The Emperor's Silent Army
Viking
Discovering a wonder of the ancient world

PARK, LINDA SUE
When My Name Was Keoko
Clarion
Korea, occupied by the Japanese military

PERKINS, MITALI
***Monsoon Summer**
Delacorte
The lessons India teaches to Jazz

POITRAS, GILLES
The Anime Companion
Stone Bridge
From Aidoro (idol) to Zori (sandals)

STAPLES, SUZANNE FISHER
Shiva's Fire
Frances Foster
Classical Indian dance demands devotion

SUE, CHUN
***Beijing Doll**
Riverhead
Sex life of a Chinese rock and roller

TALARIGO, JEFF
***The Pearl Diver**
Nan A. Talese
How leprosy shattered her life

TOER, PRAMOEDYA ANANTA
***All That is Gone**
Hyperion
Suffering and survival in Indonesia

TORTAJADA, ANA
***The Silenced Cry**
Thomas Dunne
A diary, a journey to Afghanistan

UNG, LOUNG
**First They Killed
My Father**
HarperCollins
A daughter's memories
of Cambodia

WANG, ANNIE
Lili
Random House
A Chinese rebel in an era
of danger

WHELAN, GLORIA
*Chu Ju's House
HarperCollins
A girl torn from her
Chinese family

YEP, LAWRENCE
Lady of Ch'iao Kuo
Scholastic
A 6th century princess
and diplomat

YI, MUNYOL
Our Twisted Hero
Hyperion
Pyongjo up against a bully in
Korea

Europe

ALMOND, DAVID
Counting Stars
Delacorte
18 stories recalling a writer's life

ARONSON, MARC
**Sir Walter Ralegh and
the Quest for El Dorado**
Clarion
From the English court to
the New World

**BARTOLETTI, SUSAN
CAMPBELL**
Black Potatoes
Houghton Mifflin
The story of the Great
Irish Famine

BOLOGNESE, DON
The Warhorse
Simon & Schuster
Lorenzo, 15, a Renaissance hero

BRESLIN, THERESA
Remembrance
Delacorte
Five Scottish lives changed
by WWI

CADNUM, MICHAEL
Daughter of the Wind
Orchard
Hallgerd, a Viking girl kidnapped

CASTELLANI, CHRISTOPHER
A Kiss From Maddalena
Algonquin
Longing for love in war-torn Italy

CERVANTES, MIGUEL DE
**...Don Quixote
de la Mancha;**
Charles Jarvis, translator
Oxford Univ. Pr.
A dreamer of impossible dreams

CHARLESWORTH, MONIQUE
*The Children's War
Knopf
Ilse and Nicolai, living
through WWII

CHEVALIER, TRACY
***The Lady and the
Unicorn**
Dutton
Tales hidden in medieval
tapestries

CORNWELL, BERNARD
The Archer's Tale
HarperCollins
Seeking revenge with a bow
and arrow

GIFF, PATRICIA REILLY
Nory Ryan's Song
Delacorte
Helping her family survive
the famine

GOTTFRIED, TED
The Cold War
Twenty-First Century
Soviet politics and collapse

GRAVETT, CHRISTOPHER
**The World of the
Medieval Knight**
Peter Bedrick
How they lived; how they fought

HAUTZIG, ESTHER
The Endless Steppe
HarperCollins
Growing up in Siberia

HAWES, LOUISE
*The Vanishing Point
Houghton Mifflin
Vini's emergence as a
16th c. painter

HEUSTON, KIMBERLEY
Dante's Daughter
Front Street
Antonia's journey with her
famous father

HOOPER, MARY
*Petals in the Ashes
Bloomsbury
Hannah facing horror:
the Great Fire, 1666

LEVINSON, NANCY SMILER
Magellan
Clarion
Attempting to sail around
the world

MEYER, CAROLYN
Doomed Queen Anne
Gulliver
Losing the affection of Henry VIII

MORGAN, NICOLA
*Fleshmarket
Delacorte
1822: Dr. Knox, healer
or murderer?

O'CONNOR, JOSEPH
Star of the Sea
Harcourt
Trapped on a ship with a killer

O'NEIL, JANE
**The World of the
Brontës**
Carlton
Lives and works of 3
Yorkshire sisters

ORCZY, EMMUSKA
The Scarlet Pimpernel
Pocketbook
Rescuing nobility from the
Terrorists

PRESSLER, MIRJAM
Shylock's Daughter
Phyllis Fogelman
She betrays her father and
her heritage

SHAWCROSS, WILLIAM
Queen and Country
Simon & Schuster
The fifty-year reign of Elizabeth II

SIMOEN, JAN
What About Anna?
Walker
Searching Bosnia for her
missing brother

TURNBULL, ANN
*No Shame, No Fear
Candlewick
Love despite religious
differences

WATSON, ELSA
*Maid Marian
Crown
Intrigue and romance in
medieval England

Native Americans

BRUCHAC, JOSEPH
Our Stories Remember
Fulcrum
History, culture through
storytelling
Pocahontas
Harcourt
The willful girl bringing peace

BURKS, BRIAN
Walks Alone
Harcourt
A brave Apache girl struggles
to survive

CARVELL, MARLENE
**Who Will Tell My
Brother?**
Hyperion
School mascot: pride and
prejudice

COLTON, LARRY
Counting Coup
Warner
Girls' basketball on the
Little Big Horn

DURRETT, DEANNE
Healers
Facts On File
Ancient traditions, modern skills

FREEDMAN, RUSSELL
**The Life and Death
of Crazy Horse**
Holiday House
A warrior of courage
and passion

Sammy & Juliana in Hollywood

BY BENJAMIN ALIRE SÁENZ
Cinco Puntos Press, 2004

I sat there, thinking about home. Hollywood, that was home. Las Cruces, this house I'd lived in all my life. My room no bigger than a monk's. Home was everything that could fit in my room. A bed, a desk, that's all that fit. More like a big closet, really. But it was all I'd ever known. Part of me wanted more. But part of me could have stayed in this house forever. I could still smell my mom in this house. I swear I could. My dad, he'd saved some of her clothes in his closet. Maybe that's why her smell was still in our house. My dad didn't know—that I knew about my mom's clothes.

This was home.

I wondered what it would be like to leave, what it would be like to be homesick. Maybe I was thinking about home and about leaving because I was holding a letter of acceptance in my hand. A letter from a university, a real American university. Not that it mattered. I wasn't going. I knew that, but damnit it felt good to get accepted. But it felt bad, too. I don't even know why I'd applied, a waste of time. Maybe I sometimes had these demons of optimism that just took over my body. But then, life, well, life just sort of exorcised those demons. And I was back to my serious, get-real-you're-just-a-guy-from-Hollywood attitude. That's what you needed to survive. Otherwise you'd break. Like Reyes. Maybe that's why he did heroin—because his dreams were too big. And the only way he could get at those dreams was through shooting some stuff up his veins.

KATZ, WILLIAM LOREN
Black Indians
Aladdin
A hidden heritage

LISLE, JANET TAYLOR
The Crying Rocks
Simon & Schuster
Joelle, meeting the ghosts of her past

MCMASTER, GERALD AND CLIFFORD E. TRAFZER, EDITORS
***Native Universe**
National Museum of the American Indian, Smithsonian Institution/ National Geographic
Art and culture of indigenous peoples

OCHOA, ANNETTE PIÑA; BETSY FRANCO, AND TRACI L. GOURDINE, EDITORS
Night is Gone, Day is Still Coming
Candlewick
Stories and poems by teens and young adults

PHILIP, NEIL, EDITOR
In a Sacred Manner I Live
Clarion
Looking at life with wisdom

REES, CELIA
Sorceress
Candlewick
Agnes and Mary, linked across centuries

RIDDLE, PAXTON
The Education of Ruby Loonfoot
Five Star
A conflict of cultures for an Objibwe girl

ROBINSON, EDEN
Monkey Beach
Houghton Mifflin
Spirits assist Lisamarie in this life

SMITH, ROLAND
The Last Lobo
Hyperion
Jake tries to save a wolf on the Hopi Rez

SMITH, WILLIAM JAY
The Cherokee Lottery
Curbstone
A shameful part of U.S. history in verse

STEVENS, MARCUS
***Useful Girl**
Algonquin
A journey to honor the past and find love

SULLIVAN, PAUL
Maata's Journal
Atheneum
An Inuit girl facing change in the Arctic

VIOLA, HERMAN J.
Warrior Artists
National Geographic
Recording their lives and loss of freedom

WALDMAN, NEIL
Wounded Knee
Atheneum
"A people's dream died there."
Black Elk

The Americas

CAMERON, ANN
Colibri
Farrar, Straus and Giroux
Kidnapped in Guatemala to help a beggar

DE LA GARZA, BEATRICE
Pillars of Gold and Silver
Piñata
Bianca's new home in Mexico

FALCONER, COLIN
Feathered Serpent
Three Rivers
Cortes' Aztec translator and lover

GOODMAN, JOAN ELIZABETH
Paradise
Houghton Mifflin
Lovers, stranded on a Canadian island

HERRERA, JUAN FELIPE
Thunderweavers
Univ. of Arizona Pr.
Bilingual poems of the violence
in Chiapas

JENKINS, LYLL BECERRA DE
So Loud a Silence
Lodestar
Juan, living in fear in Colombia

MARTEL, SUZANNE
The King's Daughter
Groundwood
Wed to a stranger in
Canada's wilderness

MONTEJO, VICTOR
Popol Vuh
Groundwood
The Maya-from creation
to conquest

PAULSEN, GARY
The Crossing
Orchard
Manuel, in flight from Mexico
to Texas

WISEMAN, EVA
A Place Not Home
Stoddart Kids
Escaping from Hungary to Canada

WOOD, FRANCES M.
Daughter of Madrugada
Delacorte
When Mexico lost California

WOOD, MICHAEL
Conquistadors
University of California Press
Spanish explorers in the
New World

YEE, PAUL
Dead Man's Gold
and Other Stories
Groundwood
Ten tales of relocating to
North America

Latinos

ALVAREZ, JULIA
***Finding Miracles**
Knopf
Milly, exploring her roots

BIERHORST, JOHN, EDITOR
Latin American
Folktales
Pantheon
From Hispanic and Indian
traditions

DÍAZ, JUNOT
Drown
Riverhead
Stories of Dominican youth

GONZALES ABRAHAM,
SUSAN AND DENISE
GONZALES ABRAHAM
***Cecilia's Year**
Cinco Puntos
Challenging her family's
traditional ideas

HINOJOSA, MARIA
Raising Raul
Viking
Discovering herself and her son

MARTINEZ, MANUEL LUIS
Drift
Picador
Robert, 16, on the road west
to LA

MARTINEZ, VICTOR
Parrot in the Oven
HarperCollins
Manny's family, friends and
foes in Fresno

MOHR, NICHOLASA
In Nueva York
Arte Publico
Human stories on the
Lower East Side

ORITZ COFER, JUDITH
***Call Me Maria**
Orchard
From PR to the barrio in NYC

ORTIZ COFER, JUDITH,
EDITOR
***Riding Low Through**
the Streets of Gold
Piñata
Identity, love, loss: stories
and poems

OSA, NANCY
Cuba 15
Delacorte
Violet, preparing for
her quinceañero

PEREZ-BROWN, MARIA
Mamá
Rayo
Latina daughters celebrate
their mothers

RICE, DAVID
Crazy Loco
Dial
Nine stories of Mexican
American lives

SÁENZ, BENJAMIN ALIRE
***Sammy & Juliana**
in Hollywood
Cinco Puntos
Tough life of a Chicano boy
in the 60s

SALDAÑA, RENÉ, JR.
Finding Our Way
Wendy Lamb
Dreams, drama, twelve stories

SANTANA, PATRICIA
Motorcycle Ride
on the Sea of
Tranquility
Univ. of New Mexico
Yolanda and her Mexican
American family

SANTIAGO,
ESMERALDA
Almost a Woman
Perseus
Finding her identity
in Brooklyn

VECIANA-SUAREZ,
ANA
Flight to Freedom
Orchard
A Cuban family
emigrates
to Miami, 1967

VEGA, MARTA MORENO
***When the Spirits Dance**
Mambo
Three Rivers
Growing up Nuyorican in El Barrio

VILLASEÑOR, VICTOR
***Burro Genius**
Rayo
From angry teen to
bestselling author

U.S.A.
Coming to
America

BROWN, JACKIE
***Little Cricket**
Hyperion
A Laotian girl in the Midwest

BROWN, WESLEY
Imagining America
Persea
38 stories from "The
Promised Land"

DANTICAT, EDWIDGE
Behind the Mountains
Orchard
Celiane's diary: from Haiti
to Brooklyn

GALLO, DONALD R., EDITOR
***First Crossing**
Candlewick
Stories of today's immigrant teens

GIFF, PATRICIA REILLY
Maggie's Door
Wendy Lamb
Nory travels from Ireland with
a dream

HALABY, LAILA
West of the Jordan
Beacon
Palestinian girls in America

HO, MINFONG
The Stone Goddess
Orchard
Memories of lost Cambodia

HOOBLER, DOROTHY AND
THOMAS HOOBLER
We Are Americans
Scholastic
Immigrants, in their own words

NA, AN
A Step from Heaven
Front Street
Bridging two worlds;
Korea and America

SON, JOHN
Finding My Hat
Orchard
A Korean family finding home
in the USA

Worlds Afire

BY PAUL B. JANECZKO
Candlewick, Press, 2004

BUDDY MULLENS
Twenty-Four-Hour Man

I arrive
the day before
when there is no circus,
only dreams of one
in the hearts of kids.
Without me
they would only wish
for the "Greatest Show on Earth."

They call me the "make sure guy."
I make sure the lot is laid out,
midway, menagerie,
big top, dressing tent;
make sure hay bales are stacked,
grain sacks piled,
gasoline and food delivered.

Make sure it's all there
before the train steams into town
tomorrow morning.
After I make sure
we'll be ready
for clowns
and wild beasts
and high-wire walkers,
I tramp the neighborhoods
and make sure the advance man
has plastered banners
where the kids can hear
the bright bold letters and a roaring tiger
calling them
to a show they'll never forget.

WORLDS AFIRE

Paul B. Janeczko

TELUSHKIN, JOSEPH, RABBI
The Golden Land
Harmony
The story of Jewish immigration

YEP, LAURENCE
The Traitor
HarperCollins
Wyoming, 1885, Chinese miners
in peril

ZABYTKO, IRENE
**When Luba
Leaves Home**
Algonquin
Off to college for a Ukrainian girl

U.S.A. Black America

**ABDUL-JABBAR, KAREEM
AND ANTHONY WALTON**
*Brothers in Arms
Broadway
Black soldiers at the
Battle of the Bulge

BOLDEN, TONYA
**Strong Men
Keep Coming**
Wiley
Four centuries of courage

BOYD, HERB, EDITOR
**Autobiography
of a People**
Anchor
Historical truth—
3 centuries, 116 voices

**BYRD, AYANA D. AND
LORI L. THARPS**
Hair Story
St. Martin's
600 years of locks, kinks,
and curls

CERAMI, CHARLES A.
Benjamin Banneker
Wiley & Sons
Surveyor, astronomer,
publisher, patriot

CLINTON, CATHERINE
The Black Soldier
Houghton Mifflin
From 1492 to the present

CROWE, CHRIS
**Getting Away
with Murder**
Phyllis Fogelman Books
The true story of the
Emmett Till case

**DODSON, HOWARD AND
SYLVIANE A. DIOUF,
COMPILERS AND EDITORS**
*In Motion
National Geographic
The African-American
migration experience

**DUE, TANANARIVE AND
PATRICIA STEPHENS DUE**
Freedom in the Family
One World
Mother and daughter:
the Civil Rights era

FINLAYSON, REGGIE
We Shall Overcome
Lerner
History of the civil
rights movement

FRADIN, DENNIS BRINDELL
**My Family Shall
Be Free!**
HarperCollins
One man's search for enslaved
loved ones

**HANSEN, JOYCE
AND GARY MCGOWAN**
Freedom Roads
Cricket
Searching for the
Underground Railroad

HUDSON, WADE
*Powerful Words
Scholastic Nonfiction
From Benjamin Banneker to
Lauryn Hill

KATZ, WILLIAM LOREN
Black Pioneers
Atheneum
Settlers and freedom fighters

LANDAU, ELAINE
Slave Narratives
Watts
Memoirs of those formerly
in bondage

**MCKISSACK, PATRICIA
C. AND FREDRICK L.
MCKISSACK**
**Black Hands, White
Sails**
Scholastic
Contributions to the
whaling industry

MCWORTHER, DIANE
*A Dream of Freedom
Scholastic Nonfiction
The pursuit of equality,
1954–1968

MELTZER, MILTON
Langston Hughes
Millbrook
The soul of his people
captured in poetry
There Comes a Time
Random House
The struggle for civil rights

MORRISON, JOHN
*Cornel West
Chelsea House
Public intellectual,
renaissance man

**MYERS, WALTER DEAN
AND CHRISTOPHER MYERS**
Blues Journey
Holiday House
A father and son's call
and response

NELSON, MARILYN
*Fortune's Bones
Front Street
Dead 200 years before his
name was known

REMBERT, WINFRED
Don't Hold Me Back
Cricket
Survived being lynched,
becoming an artist

ROCHELLE, BELINDA
Words with Wings
HarperCollins
A treasury of poetry and art

SHABAZZ, ILYASAH
Growing Up X
One World
A daughter of Malcolm
Shabazz speaks

TAYLOR, MILDRED D.
The Land
Penguin Putnam/Phyllis Fogelman
A young, former slave's dream

TYSON, TIMOTHY B.
***Blood Done Sign My Name**
Crown
Racist murder in a small southern town

U.S.A. Past, Present and Future

ARONSON, MARC
Witch Hunt
Atheneum
Mysteries of the Salem witch trials

BARTOLETTI, SUSAN CAMPBELL
Kids on Strike!
Houghton Mifflin
Standing up for their rights as workers

BLUMENTHAL, KAREN
Six Days in October
Atheneum
When the stock market crashed, 1929

COOPER, MICHAEL L.
***Dust to Eat**
Clarion
Drought and depression in the 1930's

FARRELL, MARY CRONK
***Fire in the Hole!**
Clarion
1899, any job but mining for Mick

FRADIN, DENNIS B. AND JUDITH BLOOM FRADIN
Ida B. Wells
Clarion
She fought for the end of lynchings

FREEDMAN, RUSSELL
In Defense of Liberty
Holiday House
The story of the Bill of Rights

GIBLIN, JAMES CROSS, EDITOR
The Century That Was
Atheneum
Explores the road we've travelled

HOLZER, HAROLD, EDITOR
Abraham Lincoln the Writer
Boyds Mills
His speeches, letters, and poetry

JACKSON, ROBERT
***Meet Me in St. Louis**
HarperCollins
The 1904 World's Fair, an extravaganza

JANECZKO, PAUL B.
***World's Afire**
Candlewick
The blaze that destroyed the circus, 1944

LANIER, SHANNON AND JANE FELDMAN
Jefferson's Children
Random House
Family reunion across racial lines

MALCOLM X AND ALEX HALEY
The Autobiography of Malcolm X
Ballantine
The Black leader's testament

MARGOLICK, DAVID
Strange Fruit
Running Press
How one song's lyrics changed the world

MCDONALD, JOYCE
***Devil on My Heels**
Delacorte
Florida, 1959: Dove, shocked to find KKK

MCKISSACK, PATRICIA AND ARLENE ZAREMBKA
***To Establish Justice**
Knopf
The basis of our liberty: The Constitution

MURPHY, JIM
An American Plague
Clarion
The yellow fever epidemic of 1793

***Inside the Alamo**
Delacorte
The battle for Texas: fact and fiction

MYERS, WALTER DEAN
***USS Constellation**
Holiday House
Pride of the United States Navy

PECK, RICHARD
Fair Weather
Dial
Country kids, a ferris wheel, and Chicago

PERL, LILA
North Across the Border
Benchmark
The journey of Mexican Americans

RUBIN, SUSAN GOLDMAN
***L'Chaim!**
Abrams
Since 1654, Jewish life in America

STEIN, STEPHEN J.
Alternative American Religions
Oxford Univ. Pr.
From the Puritans to Heaven's Gate

THOMAS, JOYCE CAROL, EDITOR
Linda Brown, You Are Not Alone
Jump at the Sun
Writers respond: Brown v. Board of Education

L'Chaim!

BY SUSAN RUBIN GOLDMAN
Harry N. Abrams, Inc., 2004

In early September, 1654, the ship *Sainte Catherine* docked at the Wharf in New Amsterdam, a Dutch town that was soon to be renamed New York. About twenty-three Jews straggled off the ship. Historians still differ as to the exact number, but agree that the group included men, women, and children. All were exhausted after their long, miserable voyage from Recife, formerly a Dutch colony in Brazil, where they could no longer practice their faith. Like the Pilgrims who had arrived on the *Mayflower* at Plymouth Rock thirty-four years earlier, they were seeking religious freedom. Unlike the Pilgrims, they did not want their own colony. Instead, they wished to live among the local residents and conduct trade.

On the way to America, the Jewish voyagers, rocking back and forth in the cramped wooden ship, had suffered from seasickness. Legends tell that pirates had attacked them and had stolen most of their money and possessions. When they finally landed in New Amsterdam, they could not pay for their expensive trip. The captain sued, forcing them to sell everything they had left to settle their debt. But the small group of Jews believed that at last they had found a safe home.

The immigrants soon discovered this was not the case.

Subways

BY LORRAINE B DIEHL
Crown, 2004

In 1868, state senator and notoriously corrupt city leader Boss Tweed decided what would and what would not be built in New York, and the only projects the graft-addicted politician allowed to rise were those that could give him a hefty slice of the pie. Beach wanted to build the city's first subway, but he knew that the man who sat in Tammany Hall, just a shadow's length from the *Sun*'s offices, would have his hand out, and Beach refused to pay him off. "I won't pay political blackmail," he told his brother. "I say, let's build it furtively."

"We propose to run the line to Central Park, about five miles in all," he would eventually proclaim. "When completed, we should be able to carry twenty thousand passengers a day at speeds up to a mile a minute." But for now there were no proclamations, just secret plans. For nineteenth-century New Yorkers, Beach's idea for a subway line was beyond comprehension. No one went down into the earth to get from one part of the city to another.

WEISS, JERRY AND HELEN S. WEISS, EDITORS
Big City Cool
Persea
14 stories of urban American youth

U.S.A. The New Nation

ARONSON, MARC
***John Winthrop, Oliver Cromwell and the Land of Promise**
Clarion
Ideas and individuals creating America

BLACKWOOD, GARY
The Year of the Hangman
Dutton
Imagining if Americans lost the war

BOBER, NATALIE S.
Countdown to Independence
Atheneum
A chronology of the years 1760–1776

BOWEN, CATHERINE DRINKER
Miracle at Philadelphia
Little, Brown
1787 convention as seen by the delegates

CLEMENS, SAMUEL L.
The Adventures of Huckleberry Finn
Penguin Putnam
Two runaways on the Mississippi

COX, CLINTON
Come All You Brave Soldiers
Scholastic
5000 Blacks in the Continental Army

FAST, HOWARD
April Morning
Bantam
A boy at the Battle of Lexington

FERRIE, RICHARD
The World Turned Upside Down
Holiday House
Washington's victory at Yorktown

FLEMING, CANDACE
Ben Franklin's Almanac
Atheneum
His countless accomplishments

GARLAND SHERRY
In the Shadow of the Alamo
Harcourt
Lorenzo, fighting for the honor of Mexico

HIRSCHFELDER, ARLENE B.
Photo Odyssey
Clarion
Documenting trails blazed to the Pacific

LAVENDER, WILLIAM
Just Jane
Harcourt
A war with loyalities and emotions

MARRIN, ALBERT
George Washington and the Founding of a Nation
Dutton
Farmer, general, president, slaveholder

RINALDI, ANN
Taking Liberty
Simon & Schuster
Oney, enslaved in a presidential home

ST. GEORGE, JUDITH
John and Abigail Adams
Holiday House
President and First Lady, a strong love

WOLF, ALLAN
***New Found Land**
Candlewick
Imagining the journey of Lewis and Clark

U.S.A. The Civil War and After

DOUGLASS, FREDERICK
Narrative of the Life of Frederick Douglass, an American Slave
Harvard
As slave and abolitionist

ELLIOTT, L. M.
***Annie, Between the States**
Katherine Tegen
A patriot of the Confederacy finds love

HAHN, MARY DOWNING
Hear the Wind Blow
Clarion
At 13, fending for himself and his sister

HANSEN, JOYCE
Bury Me Not in a Land of Slaves
Watts
Former slaves' lives during Reconstruction

HOBBS, WILL
Down the Yukon
HarperCollins
Racing to Alaska for a $20,000 prize

HOLZER, HAROLD
***The President is Shot!**
Boyds Mills
The story behind the murder of Lincoln

JILES, PAULETTE
Enemy Women
Morrow
Adair, imprisoned and plotting escape

MCKISSACK, PATRICIA C. AND FREDRICK L.
Days of Jubilee
Scholastic
The end of slavery

MCMULLAN, MARGARET
*How I Found the Strong
Houghton Mifflin
Frank's changing view of war

MCPHERSON, JAMES M.
Fields of Fury
Atheneum
A divided nation at war

PECK, RICHARD
The River Between Us
Dial
Tilly, her world was changed
by war

REEDER, CAROLYN
Before the Creeks Ran Red
HarperCollins
Bitter divisions among neighbors

RINALDI, ANN
*Sarah's Ground
Simon & Schuster
On her own, overseeing
Mount Vernon

ROBERTSON, JAMES I., JR.
Standing Like a Stone Wall
Atheneum
General Thomas J.
"Stonewall" Jackson

SCHMIDT, GARY D.
*Lizzie Bright and the Buckminster Boy
Clarion
Saving a black community
at risk

SEVERANCE, JOHN B.
Braving the Fire
Clarion
Joining the Union Army,
seeking glory

WISLER, G. CLIFTON
When Johnny Went Marching
HarperCollins
Under 18, in military service

New York, NY

DIEHL, LORRAINE B.
*Subways
Clarkson Potter
From secret tunnels to
mass transit

HAMPTON, WILBORN
September 11, 2001
Candlewick
The attack on New York
City recalled

HIDIER, TANUJA DESAI
Born Confused
Scholastic
NJ Indian girl exploring love
and NYC

HILL, LABAN CARRICK
*Harlem Stomp!
Little, Brown
A cultural history of the
Renaissance

KENNEDY, RANDY
*Subwayland
St. Martin's
The underground world
New Yorkers share

LEBLANC, ADRIAN NICOLE
Random Family
Scribner
Love, drugs and trouble
in the Bronx

MACK, TRACY
Birdland
Scholastic
Images of NYC, traces of
a dead brother

MARBERRY, CRAIG AND MICHAEL CUNNINGHAM
Spirit of Harlem
Doubleday
That most exciting neighborhood

PETIT, PHILIPPE
To Reach the Clouds
North Point
High wire walk between the
Twin Towers

QUIÑONEZ, ERNESTO
Bodega Dreams
Vintage
Chino, surviving Spanish Harlem

RODIS, LEDA AND SERGUEI BASSINE
*From the 104th Floor
Steerforth
Trapped after the attack
on the towers

SULLIVAN, ROBERT
*Rats
Bloomsbury
The city's most
undesirable tenant

THOMS, ANNIE, EDITOR
With Their Eyes
HarperTempest
September 11: voices
from Stuyvesant High

VERGARA, CAMILO JOSÉ
*Subway Memories
Monacelli Press
The trains, the stations,
the riders

VIZZINI, NED
Teen Angst? Naaah...
Free Spirit
Ned's year at
Stuyvesant
High School

WOLFMAN, IRA
Jewish New York
Universe
Landmarks,
neighborhoods,
food, people...

*new book title

Rats

BY ROBERT SULLIVAN
Bloomsbury USA, 2004

WHEN I FINALLY WENT OUT on my own to find a colony of wild New York City rats, I ended up talking to a lot of exterminators. Exterminators, or pest control technicians as they often prefer to be known, are the philosopher kings of the rat-infested world, the trap- and poison-toting mystics. I have gleaned many insights from them. Practically speaking, I have learned about the significance of spotting rats during the day. "When you see rats in the daytime, boy, the population is so large that the night feeding won't support them," one exterminator told me. "Only the dominant rats are getting enough to eat, and the weaker rats, they've gotta take a chance and go out during they day. They don't really want to be out during the day." Likewise, I learned about the strength of rats vis-à-vis cats. Here is this anecdote from an exterminator working in New York, in the borough of Queens: "A woman said to me, 'Oh, we're going to get a cat!'" he recalled. "I said, 'Miss, please don't put that cat in the cellar.' Then I came back two weeks later and I'm picking up the hair and the bones of the cat. They think it's like in the cartoons. But in the cartoons it's Tom and Jerry the *mouse*, not Tom and Jerry the *rat*!"

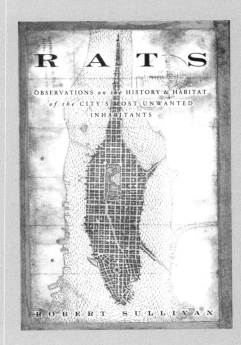

Action/Adventure

Wheels and Wings

BRINGHURST, JOHN
Planes, Jets, & Helicopters
Tab
Great paper airplanes

COLLINS, MARY
Airborne
National Geographic
The Wright Brothers: the first to fly

CROWTHER, NICKY
The Ultimate Mountain Bike Book
Firefly
How to explore all terrains

GIBLIN, JAMES CROSS
Charles A. Lindbergh
Clarion
Pilot and American hero

HULLS, JOHN
Rider in the Sky
Crown
An American cowboy's early airplane

INGOLD, JEANETTE
Airfield
Puffin
Beatty, 15, a wannabe pilot

KESSEL, ADRIENNE
The World's Strangest Automobiles
Chelsea House
Weird and wonderful cars

MILLER, TIMOTHY AND STEVE MILTON
***NASCAR Now**
Firefly
Everything about stock car racing

MIRRA, DAVE
Mirra Images
ReganBooks
A BMX champion defying gravity

MONTVILLE, LEIGH
At the Altar of Speed
Broadway
Dale Earnhardt-fast life, tragic death

RAMO, JOSHUA COOPER
No Visible Horizon
Simon & Schuster
Thrill and danger of aerial aerobatics

RINARD, JUDITH E.
Book of Flight
Firefly
From the Wright brothers to Mars

WERNER, DOUG
Skateboarder's Start Up
Tracks
Skills, thrills, history, safety

Do-It-Yourself

BOURSIN, DIDIER
Origami Paper Airplanes
Firefly
Fantastic folded flyers

BRAZELTON, BEV
***Altered Books Workshop**
North Light
Tearing, painting, gluing, transforming

CARLE, MEGAN AND JILL CARLE WITH JUDI CARLE
***Teens Cook**
Ten Speed Press
How to make what you want to eat

CHIARELLO, MARK AND TODD KLEIN
***The DC Comics Guide to Coloring and Lettering Comics**
Watson-Guptill
Elements that make the story come alive

HAAB, SHERRI
***The Hip Handbag Book**
Watson-Guptill
Creating the perfect accessory

HART, CHRISTOPHER
Manga Mania Fantasy Worlds
Watson-Guptill
Drawing knights, warriors and dragons

JANECZKO, PAUL B.
***Top Secret**
Candlewick
Codes and ciphers: make them, break them

KING, DANIEL
Chess
Kingfisher
Learn to play like a grandmaster

JAYNES, ELA AND DARREN GREENBLATT
***Planet Yumthing Do-It-Yourself**
Bantam
Projects to make your world sassier

KING, DANIEL
Chess
Kingfisher
Learn to play like a grandmaster

KLEINMAN, KATHRYN
***Birthday Cakes**
Chronicle
Creating delicious memories

MONTANO, MARK
Super Suite
Universe
Guide to creating your dream bedroom

MOSS, MARIE Y.
Hello Kitty Hello Everything!
Abrams
Purrfectly pretty collectibles

MURILLO, KATHY CANO
***The Crafty Diva's D.I.Y. Stylebook**
Watson-Guptill
Easy-to-do cool creations

OWENS, THOMAS S.
Collecting Baseball Cards
Millbrook
Buying, selling, trading

SCHWARTZ, ELLEN
I Love Yoga
Tundra
Breathe, move, relax

SECKEL, AL
**The Great Book
of Optical Illusions**
Firefly
When your eyes trick your brain

**WENGER, JENNIFER,
CAROL ABRAMS AND
MAUREEN LASHER**
***Teen Knitting Club**
Artisan
Getting into one of the
hottest hobbies

Sports

**ANDERSON, LARS
AND CHAD MILLMAN**
Pickup Artists
Verso
American street basketball

BERKOW, IRA
Court Vision
Morrow
Why famous people
love basketball

BURWELL, BRYAN
At the Buzzer
Doubleday
Greatest moments in NBA history

BUXTON, TED
Soccer Skills
Firefly
Drills on every aspect of
match play

**CHÂTAIGNEAU, GÉRARD
AND STEVE MILTON**
**Figure Skating Now,
2nd ed.**
Firefly
Pushing the limits of beauty
and speed

COFFEY, MICHAEL
***27 Men Out**
Atria
Baseball's perfect games

CORBETT, SARA
Venus to the Hoop
Doubleday
Strong, beautiful Olympic stars.

**DIXON, RAMON "TRU"
AND DAVID AROMATORIO**
**How Far Do You
Wanna Go?**
New Horizon
Inner city baseball champs

GENTILE, DEREK
Smooth Moves
Black Dog & Leventhal
Juking, jamming, hooking
and slamming

GLENN, MEL
Jump Ball
Penguin Putnam
A basketball team;
their season in poems

GOODWIN, JOY
***The Second Mark**
Simon & Schuster
Battle for Olympic gold in
pair skating

HAWK, TONY
**Between Boardslides
and Burnout.**
ReganBooks
Superstar skateboarder tours
the world

**HUEBNER, MARK AND
BRAD WILSON**
Sports Bloopers
Firefly
All-star flubs and fumbles

KISSELOFF, JEFF
**Who is Baseball's
Greatest Hitter?**
Holt
Ruth? Cobb? Mays? or...?

KRASNER, STEVEN
Play Ball Like the Pros
Peachtree
Tips from baseball stars

LANNIN, JOANNE
**A History of Basketball
for Girls and Women.**
Lerner
Passion, skill, intensity,
controversy

**LEIKER, KEN AND
MARK VANCIL, EDITORS**
Unscripted
Pocket
Inside the ring with the WWE

LEWIS, MICHAEL
Moneyball
Norton
The Oakland A's: behind
the scenes

LIBERMAN, NOAH
Glove Affairs
Triumph
Baseball's most valuable piece
of equipment

LYONS, JEFFREY
**Curveballs and
Screwballs**
Random House
Baseball questions and answers

**MACY, SUE AND JANE
GOTTESMAN**
Play Like a Girl
Holt
Celebration of women in sports

MCDANIELS III, PELLOM
**So You Want to be
a Pro?**
Addax
Do you have what it takes
to succeed?

NACE, DON
Bowling for Beginners
Sterling
How to knock down those pins

PORTER, DAVID
***Winning Gymnastics
for Girls**
Facts on File
All the skills and how to
master them

**RIPKEN, CAL, JR. AND
BILL RIPKEN WITH
LARRY BURKE**
***Play Baseball the
Ripken Way**
Random House
Illustrated guide to the
fundamentals

RYAN, JOAN
**Little Girls in Pretty
Boxes**
Warner
Rise and fall of gymnasts,
figure skaters

**STEEN, SANDRA AND
SUSAN STEEN**
Take It to the Hoop
Twenty-First Century
100 years of women's
basketball

SWISSLER, BECKY
***Winning Lacrosse
for Girls**
Facts on File
How to excel at this
high-speed sport

**TOMLINSON, JOE WITH
ED LEIGH**
***Extreme Sports**
Firefly
Attitude, individuality, no limits

WILSON, LESLIE
**The Ultimate Guide
to Cheerleading**
Three Rivers
Stunts, jumps and chants

Athletes

**ARMSTRONG, LANCE
WITH SALLY JENKINS**
**Every Second
Counts**
Broadway
Tour de France winner,
cancer survivor

COFFEY, WAYNE
**Winning Sounds
Like This**
Crown
Women's basketball
at Gallaudet

COX, LYNNE
***Swimming to
Antarctica**
Knopf
Tales of a long-distance
swimmer

Hoop Kings
BY CHARLES R. SMITH, JR.
Candlewick Press, 2004

Allen Iverson:
By Any Means Necessary

Crooked cornrows
cause chaotic
and catastrophic collisions
with precision.
Your mission
and goal:
put the ball
in the hole
using lightning-quick speed
and total body control.
Tattooed warrior
sinking shots legendary
putting up points
by any means necessary...

Poems by
Charles R.
Smith Jr.

CROTHERS, TIM AND JOHN GARRITY
Greatest Athletes of the 20th Century
Total/Sports Illustrated
Ali, Jordan, Ruth, and others

The Definitive Word on Michael Jordan.
Beckett
The best there ever was

DE ANGELIS, GINA
Jackie Robinson
Chelsea House
First black in baseball's major leagues

GOTTLIEB, ANDREW
In the Paint
Hyperion
Tattoos of the NBA and what they signify

HAMM, MIA
Go for the Goal
HarperCollins
The soccer champion's guide to winning

JETER, DEREK
Game Day
Crown
What it's like to be a Yankee superstar

JONES, RYAN
King James
St. Martin's
Basketball phenom, LeBron James

LALLY, RICHARD
Bombers
Crown
Eyewitness accounts of Yankee history

LOUGANIS, GREG WITH ERIC MARCUS
Breaking the Surface
Dutton
Olympic diving champion tells all

MACDONALD, ANDY WITH THERESA FOY DIGERONIMO
Dropping in With Andy Mac
Simon Pulse
Daredevil antics of a pro-skateboarder

MARTIN, MARVIN
Arthur Ashe
Scholastic
His impact on and off the tennis court

OHNO, APOLO ANTON
A Journey
S & S
Olympic gold medal skater, age 20

O'NEAL, SHAQUILLE
Shaq Talks Back
St.Martin's
An honest look at himself and the NBA

RAPOPORT, RON
See How She Runs
Algonquin
Marion Jones: fastest woman in the world

SLATER, KELLY WITH JASON BORTE
Pipe Dreams
ReganBooks
Six-time world champion surfer

SMITH, CHARLES R., JR.
*Hoop Kings
Candlewick
Odes to twelve top players

SOSA, SAMMY WITH MARCOS BRETÓN
Sosa
Warner
How he became a record-breaking slugger

STARKS, JOHN WITH DAN MARKOWITZ
*John Starks: My Life
Sports Publishing
From tough times to the NBA

STREGE, JOHN
Tiger
Broadway
Golf's first black star

TESSITORE, JOHN
Muhammad Ali
Scholastic
The only three-time heavyweight champ

Action-Packed Stories

BRADLEY, KIMBERLY
Halfway to the Sky
Delacorte
Lessons learned on the Appalachian Trail

CHILD, LINCOLN
Utopia
Doubleday
A futuristic theme park gone haywire

CRUTCHER, CHRIS
Whale Talk
Greenwillow
A swim team made up of misfits!

DEUKER, CARL
High Heat
Houghton Mifflin
Pitching as life falls apart

ESCKILSEN, ERIK E.
*Offsides
Houghton Mifflin
When the team's mascot is offensive

GRISHAM, JOHN
Bleachers
Doubleday
Football coach who changed kids lives

HOBBS, WILL
*Leaving Protection
HarperCollins
Finding danger, fishing off Alaska's coast

HOROWITZ, ANTHONY
*Eagle Strike
Philomel
Teen spy trying to stop a madman

KARR, KATHLEEN
Bone Dry
Hyperion
Scanning the Sahara for clues to the past

KLASS, DAVID
Home of the Brave
Frances Foster
How a "phenom" shakes up
the soccer team

LIPSYTE, ROBERT
The Contender
HarperCollins
Using boxing to survive

LUPICA, MIKE
***Travel Team**
Philomel
Danny, seeking victory
in basketball

MEYER, L.A.
Bloody Jack
Harcourt
Disguised as a boy to sail
the seas

MORPURGO, MICHAEL
Kensuke's Kingdom
Scholastic
Alone on a not totally
deserted island

ODHIAMBO, DAVID
***Kipligat's Chance**
St. Martin's
Running rivals from Kenya

PAULSEN, GARY
Brian's Hunt
Wendy Lamb
Avenging a bear attack

PETERSEN, P.J.
Rising Water
Simon & Schuster
Dangerous encounters after
a flood

RITTER, JOHN H.
**The Boy Who Saved
Baseball**
Philomel
One game deciding the fate
of a town

SALISBURY, GRAHAM
Lord of the Deep
Delacorte
Learning the ropes on the
high seas

WALLACE, RICH
Losing Is Not An Option
Knopf
Life of a small-town jock

True Adventure

DAVIS, JILL, EDITOR
Open Your Eyes
Viking
What writers learned in
faraway places

EDINGER, RAY
Fury Beach
Berkley
Icebound in the Canadian Arctic

FERRERAS, PIPIN
***The Dive**
Regan
True love at incredible depths

GORE, ARIEL
**Atlas of the
Human Heart**
Seal
At 16, wandering the world

KING, DEAN
***Skeletons on
the Zahara**
Little, Brown
Shipwrecked; then enslaved

KURSON, ROBERT
***Shadow Divers**
Random House
Secrets in a sunken WWII
German U-boat

MYERS, WALTER DEAN
***Antarctica**
Scholastic
Expeditions to the bottom
of the world

RALSTON, ARON
***Between a Rock
and a Hard Place**
Atria
Hiking alone, trapped by a boulder

**RENNER, ELMER AND
KENNETH BIRKS**
***Sea of Sharks**
Naval Institute
On a raft in the pacific
in a typhoon

RIDGEWAY, RICK
***The Big Open**
National Geographic
On foot across Tibet to
save wildlife

RIFFENBURGH, BEAU
***Shackleton's
Forgotten Expedition**
Bloomsbury
His first trip to the Antarctic

**SALISBURY, GAY AND
LANEY SALISBURY**
The Cruelest Miles
Norton
Racing across Alaska to
save lives

TAYLER, JEFFREY
**Glory in a
Camel's Eye**
Houghton Mifflin
Trekking through the
Moroccan desert

**VENABLES,
STEPHEN**
To the Top
Candlewick
The challenge of
climbing Everest

*new book title

Between a Rock and a Hard Place

BY ARON RALSTON
Atria, 2004

I try not to think about the fact that I am stuck. Though it's an irrepressible reality, thinking about it doesn't help my situation. Instead, I concentrate on finding small weaknesses in the face of the boulder just above and to the left of my trapped right wrist. My earlier instincts led me to etch a demarcation line above the softball-sized volume of rock that I have decided I must eradicate to gain my freedom. I'm speculating on a flaw in the rock's structure, in a slight concavity that's above the bulge almost six inches from my wrist; the demarcation line runs through this concavity. I start at my line, high on the face of the rock but a few inches below the top, and hack downward, attacking as near to my mark as I can manage. Tapping, then pounding, my multi-tool's three-inch stainless-steel blade against the stone, I try to hit the same spot with each strike.

Everything else — the pain, the thoughts of rescue, the accident itself — recedes. I'm taking action. My mind seems determined to find and exploit any seams or natural cleavage of the chockstone to hasten the removal of material. Every few minutes, I pause to look over the boulder's entire surface to make sure I'm not missing a more obvious target.

But the going is imperceptibly slow.

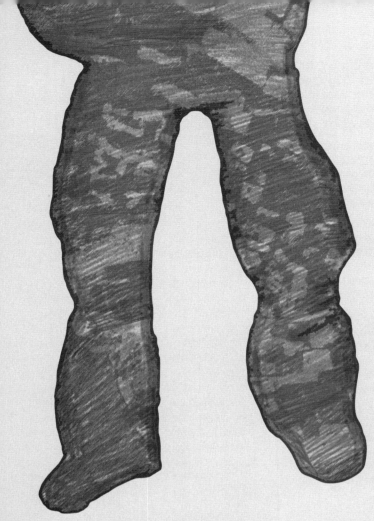

Branch Libraries

Manhattan

Aguilar
174 East 110th St.

Andrew Heiskell Braille and Talking Book Library
40 West 20th St.

Bloomingdale
150 West 100th St.

Terence Cardinal Cooke-Cathedral
560 Lexington Ave.

Chatham Square
33 East Broadway

Columbus
742 10th Ave.

Countee Cullen
104 West 136th St.

Donnell Library Center
20 West 53rd St.

Epiphany
228 East 23rd St.

Fifty-Eighth Street
127 East 58th St.

Fort Washington
535 West 179th St.

George Bruce
518 West 125th St.

Hamilton Fish Park
415 East Houston St.

Hamilton Grange
503 West 145 St.

Harlem
9 West 124th St.

Hudson Park
66 Leroy St.

Inwood
4790 Broadway

Jefferson Market
425 Ave. of the Americas

Kips Bay
446 Third Ave.

Macomb's Bridge
2650 Adam Clayton Powell, Jr. Blvd.

Mid-Manhattan Library
455 Fifth Ave.

Morningside Heights
2900 Broadway

Muhlenberg
209 West 23rd St.

Nathan Straus Teen Central Donnell Library Center
20 West 53rd St.

New Amsterdam
9 Murray St.

The New York Public Library for the Performing Arts
40 Lincoln Center Plaza

96th Street
112 East 96th St.

115th Street
2011 Adam Clayton Powell, Jr. Blvd Temporary Site

125th Street
224 East 125th St.

Ottendorfer
135 Second Ave.

Riverside
127 Amsterdam Ave.

Roosevelt Island
524 Main St.

St. Agnes
444 Amsterdam Ave.

Seward Park
192 East Broadway

67th Street
328 East 67th St.

Tompkins Square
331 East 10th St.

Washington Heights
1000 St. Nicholas Ave.

Webster
1465 York Ave.

Yorkville
222 East 79th St.